Higher

Human Biology

2004 Exam

2005 Exam

2006 Exam

2007 Exam

2008 Exam

Leckie×Leckie

First exam published in 2004.
Published by Leckie & Leckie Ltd, 3rd Floor, 4 Queen Street, Edinburgh EH2 1JE
tel: 0131 220 6831 fax: 0131 225 9987 enquiries@leckieandleckie.co.uk www.leckieandleckie.co.uk

ISBN 978-1-84372-681-4

A CIP Catalogue record for this book is available from the British Library.

Leckie & Leckie is a division of Huveaux plc.

Leckie & Leckie is grateful to the copyright holders, as credited at the back of the book, for permission to use their material.
Every effort has been made to trace the copyright holders and to obtain their permission for the use of copyright material.
Leckie & Leckie will gladly receive information enabling them to rectify any error or omission in subsequent editions.

[BLANK PAGE]

FOR OFFICIAL USE

Total for
Sections B & C

X009/301

NATIONAL
QUALIFICATIONS
2004

WEDNESDAY, 19 MAY
1.00 PM – 3.30 PM

HUMAN BIOLOGY
HIGHER

Fill in these boxes and read what is printed below.

Full name of centre

Town

Forename(s)

Surname

Date of birth

Day Month Year

Scottish candidate number

Number of seat

SECTION A—Questions 1–30

Instructions for completion of Section A are given on page two.

SECTIONS B AND C

1 (a) All questions should be attempted.

(b) It should be noted that in **Section C** questions 1 and 2 each contain a choice.

2 The questions may be answered in any order but all answers are to be written in the spaces provided in this answer book, and must be written clearly and legibly in ink.

3 Additional space for answers and rough work will be found at the end of the book. If further space is required, supplementary sheets may be obtained from the invigilator and should be inserted inside the **front** cover of this book.

4 The numbers of questions must be clearly inserted with any answers written in the additional space.

5 Rough work, if any should be necessary, should be written in this book and then scored through when the fair copy has been written.

6 Before leaving the examination room you must give this book to the invigilator. If you do not, you may lose all the marks for this paper.

SCOTTISH
QUALIFICATIONS
AUTHORITY

SECTION A

Read carefully

1 Check that the answer sheet provided is for Human Biology Higher (Section A).

2 Fill in the details required on the answer sheet.

3 In this section a question is answered by indicating the choice A, B, C or D by a stroke made in **ink** in the appropriate place in the answer sheet—see the sample question below.

4 For each question there is only **one** correct answer.

5 Rough working, if required, should be done only on this question paper—or on the rough working sheet provided—**not** on the answer sheet.

6 At the end of the examination the answer sheet for Section A **must** be placed **inside** this answer book.

Sample Question

The digestive enzyme pepsin is most active in the

A mouth

B stomach

C duodenum

D pancreas.

The correct answer is **B**—stomach. A **heavy** vertical line should be drawn joining the two dots in the appropriate box in the column headed **B** as shown in the example on the answer sheet.

If, after you have recorded your answer, you decide that you have made an error and wish to make a change, you should cancel the original answer and put a vertical stroke in the box you now consider to be correct. Thus, if you want to change an answer D to an answer B, your answer sheet would look like this:

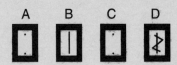

If you want to change back to an answer which has already been scored out, you should enter a tick (✓) to the **right** of the box of your choice, thus:

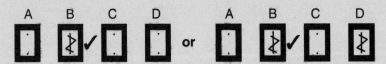

SECTION A

All questions in this section should be attempted.

Answers should be given on the separate answer sheet provided.

1. In respiration, the sequence of reactions resulting in the conversion of glucose to pyruvic acid is called

   A   the Krebs cycle

   B   the citric acid cycle

   C   glycolysis

   D   the cytochrome chain.

2. Which of the following is an insoluble polysaccharide?

   A   Glycogen

   B   Glucose

   C   Sucrose

   D   Maltose

3. Which of the following is **not** a function of lipids?

   A   Nerve insulation

   B   Vitamin transport

   C   Energy storage

   D   Oxygen transport

4. Which of the following processes requires infolding of the cell membrane?

   A   Diffusion

   B   Phagocytosis

   C   Active transport

   D   Osmosis

5. The formation of new viruses involves the following stages:

   X   viral protein coats are synthesised

   Y   host cell metabolism is taken over by virus

   Z   viral nucleic acid is replicated.

   The correct order in which these stages occur is

   A   X → Z → Y

   B   Y → X → Z

   C   Z → X → Y

   D   Y → Z → X.

6. A sex-linked gene carried on the X-chromosome of a man will be transmitted to

   A   50% of his male children

   B   50% of his female children

   C   100% of his male children

   D   100% of his female children.

7. The family tree shows the inheritance of red-green colour blindness in humans. Red-green colour blindness is a recessive, sex-linked condition.

   ○   unaffected female

   ●   affected female

   □   unaffected male

   ■   affected male

   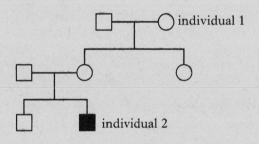

   Which line in the table describes correctly the genotypes of individual 1 and individual 2?

	Individual 1	Individual 2
A	$X^R X^R$	$X^R Y$
B	$X^R X^r$	$X^R Y$
C	$X^r X^r$	$X^r Y$
D	$X^R X^r$	$X^r Y$

   [Turn over

8. Which of the following describes the term non-disjunction?

   A   The failure of chromosomes to separate at meiosis

   B   The independent assortment of chromosomes at meiosis

   C   The exchange of genetic information at chiasmata

   D   An error in the replication of DNA before cell division

9. The diagram below shows a cross-section of a testis.

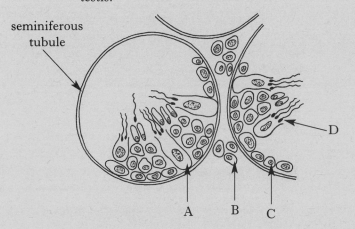

seminiferous tubule

Which cell can produce testosterone?

10. The graph below shows the growth, in length, of a human fetus before birth.

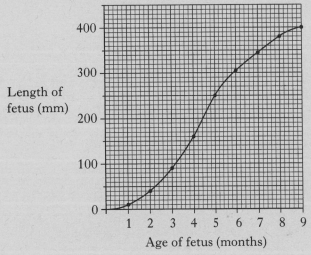

Length of fetus (mm)

Age of fetus (months)

What is the percentage increase in length of the fetus during the final 4 months of pregnancy?

   A   33·3

   B   60·0

   C   62·5

   D   150·0

11. The graph below shows the dissociation curves for fetal and maternal haemoglobin.

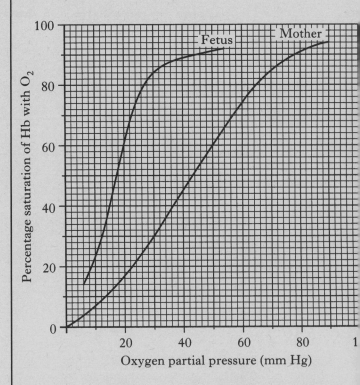

Percentage saturation of Hb with O_2

Oxygen partial pressure (mm Hg)

What is the difference in percentage saturation of haemoglobin between the mother and the fetus at a partial pressure of 30 mm Hg?

   A   18

   B   19

   C   52

   D   54

12. Which of the following are required for red blood cell production?

   A   Iron and vitamin D

   B   Calcium and vitamin B_{12}

   C   Iron and vitamin B_{12}

   D   Calcium and vitamin D

13. Colostrum provides a baby with

   A   antibodies

   B   antigens

   C   phagocytes

   D   lymphocytes.

14. The graph shows changes in lung volume during a breathing exercise.

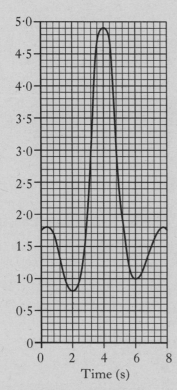

Lung volume (litres)

Time (s)

What is the volume of air inhaled between 2 and 4 seconds?

A 0·8 litres

B 3·9 litres

C 4·1 litres

D 4·9 litres

15. Which **two** blood vessels are involved in the transport of blood to and from the head?

A Carotid artery and jugular vein

B Renal artery and pulmonary vein

C Aorta and renal vein

D Hepatic artery and jugular vein

16. The table below shows the relative concentrations of certain substances in blood vessels leading to and from the liver.

(+++ = high, ++ = moderate, + = low)

Blood vessel	Oxygen	Carbon dioxide	Urea	Amino acids
1	+++	+	+	+
2	+	+++	+	+++
3	+	+++	+++	+

Which line of the table below identifies correctly the blood vessels?

	Hepatic vein	Hepatic portal vein	Hepatic artery
A	1	2	3
B	2	3	1
C	3	2	1
D	3	1	2

17. Which line of the table identifies correctly the hormones which stimulate the inter-conversion of glucose and glycogen?

	glucose → glycogen	glycogen → glucose
A	insulin	glucagon and adrenaline
B	glucagon and insulin	adrenaline
C	adrenaline and glucagon	insulin
D	adrenaline	glucagon and insulin

[Turn over

18. Which of the following shows the substance from which urea is produced and the site of urea production?

	Substance	Site of production
A	amino acid	liver
B	amino acid	kidney
C	glycogen	liver
D	glycogen	kidney

19. What is the function of the glomerulus in the production of urine?

A   Collection of filtrate

B   Filtration of blood

C   Reabsorption of glucose

D   Osmoregulation

20. The concentration of urea in plasma and urine is given in the table below.

	Plasma	Urine
Urea (g/100 cm^3)	0·3	1·29

By how many times has the urea been concentrated by the activity of the kidney?

A   0·23 times

B   0·39 times

C   4·3 times

D   43 times

21. The diagram below shows a body shape made up of cubes.

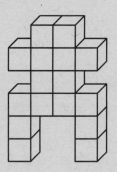

The surface area to volume ratio of this body is

A   4 : 1

B   6 : 1

C   15 : 4

D   29 : 8

22. The temperature monitoring centre of the brain is in the

A   medulla oblongata

B   cerebellum

C   pituitary gland

D   hypothalamus.

23. The diagram below shows the body's response to temperature change.

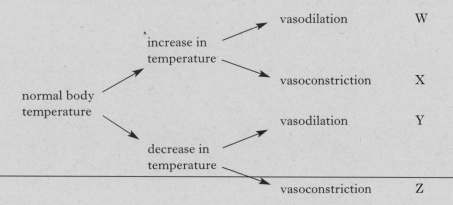

Which letters indicate negative feedback control of body temperature?

A   W and Y

B   W and Z

C   X and Y

D   X and Z

24. The peripheral nervous system contains the

A   brain and spinal cord

B   brain and somatic system

C   spinal cord and autonomic system

D   somatic system and autonomic system.

25. An investigation was carried out to determine how long it takes a student to learn the pathway through a finger maze. The student was allowed to complete the maze ten times. Which of the following pairs of factors would have to be kept the same each time?

A   The time taken to complete the maze and the shape of the maze

B   The number of errors made and the finger used

C   The finger used and the shape of the maze

D   The time taken to complete the maze and the finger used

26. Which of the following best describes social facilitation?

A   Improved performance in the presence of others

B   Deindividuation in competitive situations

C   Discrimination behaviour shown by groups of individuals

D   Shaping behaviour as seen in trial and error learning

27. Why do humans have a long period of dependency?

A   To allow for learning and the development of language

B   To allow bonding to take place between mother and child

C   To allow for the learning of motor and sensory skills

D   To allow for the growth of the brain and other major body organs

28. The diagram below shows the carbon cycle.

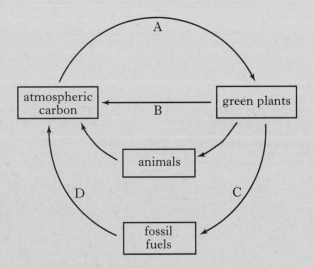

Which letter represents respiration?

[Turn over

29. In the nitrogen cycle, which of the following processes is carried out by nitrifying bacteria?

The conversion of

A   nitrate to ammonia

B   ammonia to nitrate

C   nitrogen gas to ammonia

D   nitrogen gas to nitrate.

30. An algal bloom in a loch may result from

A   lack of oxygen

B   lack of sunlight

C   excess phosphates

D   excess herbicide.

Candidates are reminded that the answer sheet MUST be returned INSIDE the front cover of this answer booklet.

SECTION B

All questions in this section should be attempted.

Marks

1. The diagram shows the role of ATP in cell metabolism.

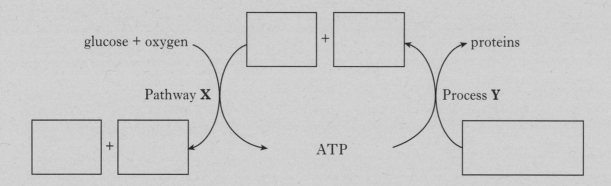

(a) Complete the diagram by entering the names of the appropriate substances.   **3**

(b)   (i)   Name **one** stage of pathway **X** and state where it occurs in the cell.

Stage _____ Location _____   **1**

(ii)   Name the organelle where process **Y** occurs.

_____   **1**

(c) Describe **two** ways in which the diagram would be different under anaerobic conditions.

1 _____

_____

2 _____

_____   **2**

(d) Name a respiratory substrate other than glucose.

_____   **1**

[Turn over

Marks

2. Sickle-cell anaemia is a blood disorder in which haemoglobin is malformed.

The diagram below shows the effect of this disorder on a red blood cell.

Normal red blood cell   Sickled red blood cell

The condition is not sex-linked. The allele for normal haemoglobin (**H**) is incompletely dominant to the sickle-cell allele (**h**).

Heterozygous individuals are mildly affected, whereas those with genotype **hh** are severely affected.

Two mildly affected parents have two children who are mildly affected like their parents. The parents are expecting a third child.

(*a*) Complete the Punnett square to show the possible genotypes of this child.

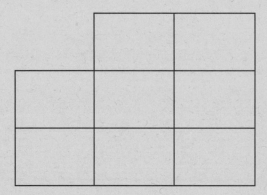

2

(*b*) From the Punnett square calculate the percentage chance of the child being

1   unaffected   _____

2   mildly affected   _____

3   severely affected.   _____

1

Marks

3. The diagram below shows a section through a lymph node.

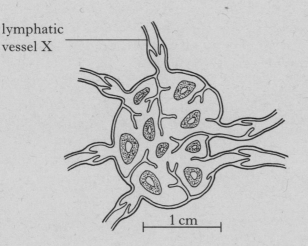

lymphatic
vessel X

1 cm

(a) Complete the table to name the cells found in the node, and to describe their functions.

Type of cell	Secretion of antibodies (yes/no)	Type of response
B-lymphocyte		
	no	cell-mediated response
		non-specific response

3

(b) Add an arrow to the diagram to indicate the direction of flow of lymph in vessel X. Give a reason for your choice.

Reason _____

_____ 1

(c) Describe **one** way in which the composition of lymph differs from plasma.

_____

_____ 1

(d) What eventually happens to the lymph after it leaves the gland?

_____ 1

(e) Describe **one** function of the lymphatic system, apart from protecting the body from infection.

_____

_____ 1

Marks

4. An investigation was carried out into the effect of caffeine on blood pressure, using coffee as the source of caffeine.

The systolic and diastolic blood pressures of six students were measured using a digital sphygmomanometer. Each student was then given a cup of coffee to drink. After one hour their blood pressure was measured again.

The results are shown in the table below.

Student	Initial blood pressure (mmHg)	Final blood pressure (mmHg)
1	120/75	134/82
2	127/79	145/88
3	118/70	124/72
4	134/81	143/83
5	122/73	133/77
6	129/84	137/90
Average	**125/77**	

(a) Calculate the average final blood pressure and write your answer in the table above.

Space for calculation

1

(b) What conclusion can be drawn from these results?

_____

_____ 1

(c) Describe an appropriate control for this investigation.

_____

_____ 1

(d) Apart from leaving one hour between readings, list **two** other variables which would need to be kept constant during this investigation.

1 _____

2 _____ 1

Marks

4. **(continued)**

   (*e*) What is meant by systolic and diastolic blood pressure?

   Systolic _____

   _____

   Diastolic_____

   _____   **2**

   (*f*) The graphs below show initial and final blood pressures of one of the students.

   Graph 1 Initial Blood Pressure   **Graph 2 Final Blood Pressure**

   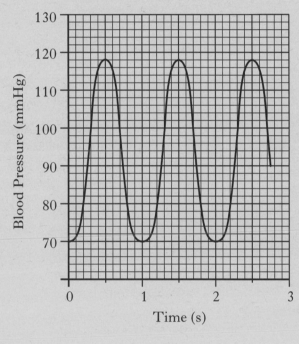   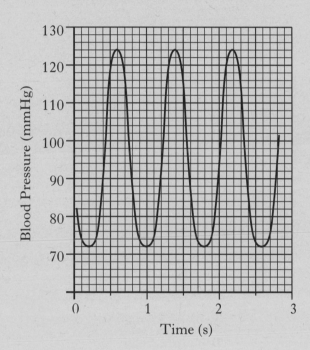

   (i) Use the information in the table and the graphs to identify the student.

   Student number _____   **1**

   (ii) Calculate the increase in the pulse rate of this student over the period of the investigation.

   Space for calculation

   _____ bpm   **1**

   [Turn over

Marks

5. The diagram shows stages in the development of a human embryo from fertilisation to implantation.

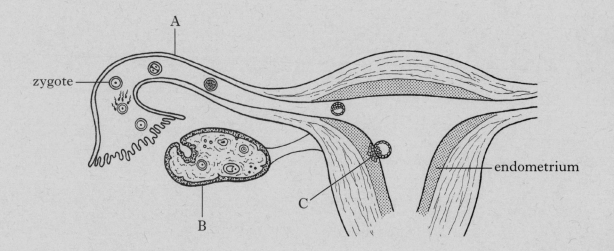

(a) Name the parts labelled **A** and **B**.

A _____ B _____ 1

(b) What term is used to describe the first few divisions of the zygote?

_____ 1

(c) Name a hormone which is involved in preparing the endometrium for implantation and state where it is produced.

Hormone _____ Produced by_____ 1

(d) What organ will develop from the tissue labelled **C**?

_____ 1

(e) Sometimes twins develop in the uterus. Distinguish between the formation of monozygotic and dizygotic twins.

_____

_____

_____

_____

_____

_____

_____ 3

Marks

6. The sperm counts of 30 men taken between 1940 and 2000 are shown in the graph below. A line of best-fit has been drawn, to indicate the trend over the 60-year period.

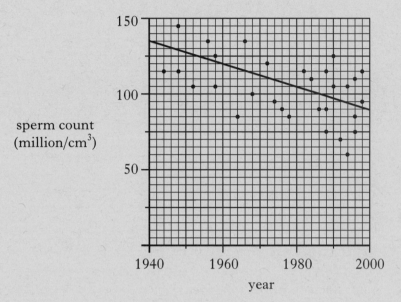

sperm count
(million/cm^3)

year

(a) Using the line of best-fit, calculate the percentage decline in sperm count over the 60-year period.

Space for calculation

_____ %   1

(b) From the graph, what is the maximum sperm count for any one individual recorded during this period?

_____ million/cm^3 1

(c) Some insecticides are thought to influence sperm production. Explain why animals at the end of food chains are more likely to be affected by insecticides.

_____

_____

_____   1

(d) Name the pituitary hormone which stimulates the production of sperm.

_____   1

[Turn over

Marks

6. **(continued)**

(e) Name a gland which adds fluid to sperm during ejaculation and describe **one** function of this fluid.

Gland _____

1

Function of fluid _____

_____

1

(f) Two treatments sometimes used for infertility are artificial insemination and *in vitro* fertilisation. Describe briefly what is meant by these terms.

artificial insemination _____

_____

in vitro fertilisation _____

_____

2

Marks

7. The Rhesus blood group system is determined by three pairs of alleles: **Cc**, **Dd** and **Ee**. However, only the **D** allele is important in blood transfusion and pregnancy. People with the dominant allele **D** are Rhesus positive and those with genotype **dd** are Rhesus negative.

(*a*) What term is used to describe characteristics controlled by many pairs of alleles?

_____   1

(*b*) Name another blood group system which has to be matched for blood transfusion to be successful.

_____   1

(*c*) What part of a cell carries the Rhesus antigen?

_____   1

(*d*) A Rhesus negative woman and a Rhesus positive man are planning to have a child. They consult a genetics counsellor to find out whether their child is likely to be Rhesus positive or Rhesus negative.

What genetic information could they be given?

_____

_____

_____

_____

_____

_____   2

(*e*) Describe a treatment which can be used to protect a child at risk from the Rhesus reaction.

_____

_____

_____   1

[Turn over

8. The table below gives data on kidney transplants for the UK in the year 2001.

Category of patient	Number
On waiting list at beginning of 2001	6052
Received transplants during the year	
Removed from the list during the year	293
Died during the year	203
Added to the list during the year	1921
On waiting list at end of 2001	6241

(a) Complete the table by calculating the number of patients who received a transplant during the year 2001.

Space for calculation

1

(b) Assuming the same trend for the year 2002, predict the number of patients on the waiting list at the end of that year.

Space for calculation

_____ 1

(c) Drugs which suppress the immune system are given to transplant patients. Explain how this treatment reduces the chance of rejection of the transplanted kidney.

_____

_____

_____

_____ 2

(d) Name the **two** blood vessels which would have to be cut and reconnected during a kidney operation.

_____ and _____ 1

Marks

9. The diagram below is of a motor homunculus which represents the relative sizes of parts of the brain associated with motor control.

(a) In which part of the brain is the motor area located?

_____   1

(b) What is the function of the motor area of the brain?

_____   1

(c) Explain why the hands have such a large area of the brain devoted to their control in comparison to the feet.

_____

_____   1

(d) What type of neural pathway is used to co-ordinate movements of the fingers?

_____   1

(e) Three facial expressions are shown below.

What term describes this type of communication?

_____   1

DO NOT
WRITE IN
THIS
MARGIN

Marks

10. The diagram shows a neuromuscular junction.

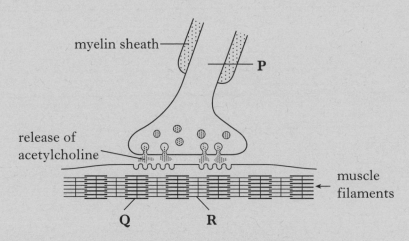

myelin sheath

P

release of
acetylcholine

muscle
filaments

Q   **R**

(*a*)   Name the part of the nerve cell labelled **P**.

_____   1

(*b*)   (i)   What kind of substance is acetylcholine?

_____   1

(ii)   What triggers the release of acetylcholine?

_____

_____   1

(iii)   State what happens to acetylcholine after it has acted on the muscle.

_____

_____   1

(*c*)   Name the **two** muscle proteins labelled **Q** and **R**.

Q _____   R _____   1

(*d*)   Describe what happens to these protein filaments when a muscle contracts.

_____

_____   1

Marks

11. Cod have been caught off the coast of Scotland for many years. The graph below shows the estimated population of cod in an area of the North Sea over the last hundred years.

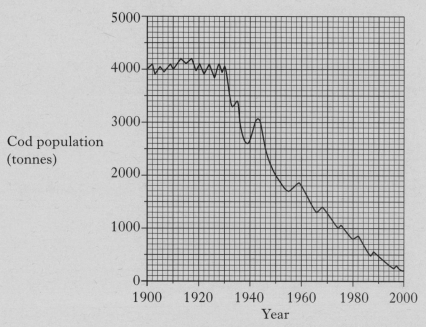

Cod population (tonnes) — Year

(*a*) Between the years 1900 and 1930 this area of the North Sea was at its carrying capacity for the cod population.

Explain what is meant by the term "carrying capacity".

_____

_____   1

(*b*) (i) Express, as a simple whole number ratio, the size of the cod population in 1950 to its size in 2000.

Space for calculation

_____ : _____   1

(ii) Suggest **two** reasons for the decline of the cod population over the last 50 years.

1 _____

_____

2 _____

_____   2

[Turn over

Marks

12. The graphs show the changes in birth and death rates of two countries **A** and **B**.

Country A

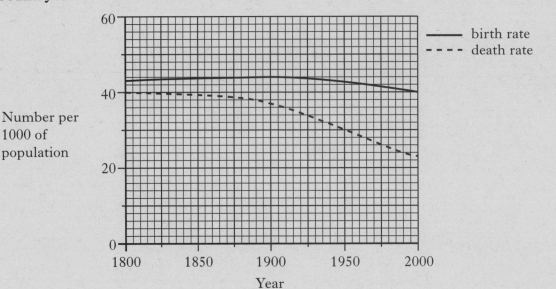

Country B

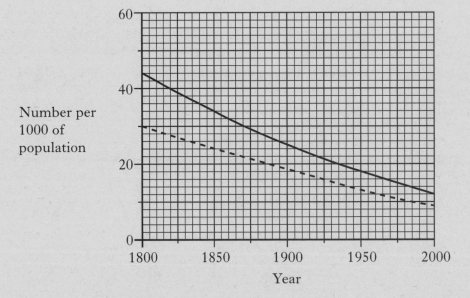

(*a*) (i) State the birth rate and death rate in country **A** in the year 1900.

Birth rate _____ Death rate _____ number per 1000   1

(ii) Suggest **one** reason for the decline in birth rate of country **A** over the last fifty years.

_____

_____   1

(iii) Suggest **one** reason for the decline in death rate of country **A** over the last fifty years.

_____

_____   1

DO NOT WRITE IN THIS MARGIN

12. (continued) *Marks*

(*b*) Is the population of country **B** increasing or decreasing over the period of time shown?

Give a reason for your answer.

Change ______________________

Reason ____

____

____ 1

(*c*) Which of the **two** countries is likely to be a developing country?

Give a reason for your answer.

Country ______________________

Reason ____

____

____ 1

[Turn over

Marks

13. An investigation was carried out into the effect of lack of nitrates on the growth of cress seedlings. Two equal batches of seeds were grown in agar gel containing:

A all necessary mineral salts

B all mineral salts except nitrate.

Each seed was placed on the surface of the agar in a glass tube as shown in the diagram below.

The heights of the seedlings were measured every day for eight days and the results are shown in the table.

Day	Average height of seedlings in gel A (mm)	Average height of seedlings in gel B (mm)
0	0	0
1	1	1
2	3	3
3	6	4
4	9	5
5	13	6
6	18	7
7	23	8
8	29	8

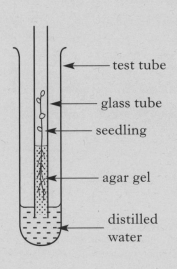

(*a*) Construct a line graph to illustrate the data in the table.

(Additional graph paper, if required, can be found on page 32.)

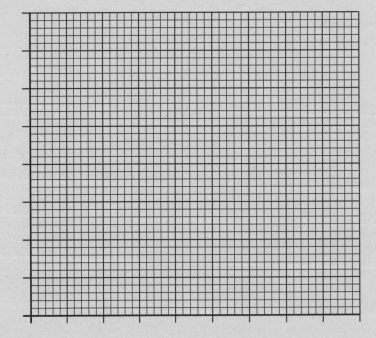

3

(*b*) State **one** conclusion which can be drawn from these results.

_____

_____

1

DO NOT WRITE IN THIS MARGIN

Marks

13. (continued)

(*c*) Identify the control and explain your choice.

Control ________________________

Explanation ____

____ 1

(*d*) What feature of this investigation makes the results reliable?

____ 1

(*e*) Suggest why distilled water is used in the test-tube rather than tap water.

____

____ 1

(*f*) Phosphates are also necessary for good plant growth. Name **one** compound, other than ADP and ATP, which contains phosphate.

______________________________ 1

[Turn over

DO NO'
WRITE
THIS
MARGI

Marks

SECTION C

Both questions in this section should be attempted.

Note that each question contains a choice.

Questions 1 and 2 should be attempted on the blank pages which follow.

Supplementary sheets, if required, may be obtained from the invigilator.

Labelled diagrams may be used where appropriate.

1. Answer **either** A **or** B.

    A. Give an account of memory under the following headings:

        (i)   short term memory;   **4**

        (ii) methods of transfer to long term memory.   **6**

                                               (10)

    OR

    B. Describe ways in which food production has been increased in the last fifty years under the following headings:

        (i)   land use;   **4**

        (ii) the use of chemicals.   **6**

                                               (10)

In question 2 ONE mark is available for coherence and ONE mark is available for relevance.

2. Answer **either** A **or** B.

    A. Describe the events in meiosis which give rise to variation in gametes.   **(10)**

    OR

    B. Describe how proteins are assembled from the code on a mRNA strand.   **(10)**

[END OF QUESTION PAPER]

SPACE FOR ANSWERS

Page twenty-seven **[Turn over**

DO NOT
WRITE IN
THIS
MARGIN

SPACE FOR ANSWERS

DO NOT
WRITE
THIS
MARGI

SPACE FOR ANSWERS

[Turn over

SPACE FOR ANSWERS

SPACE FOR ANSWERS

[Turn over

SPACE FOR ANSWERS

ADDITIONAL GRAPH PAPER FOR QUESTION 13(*a*)

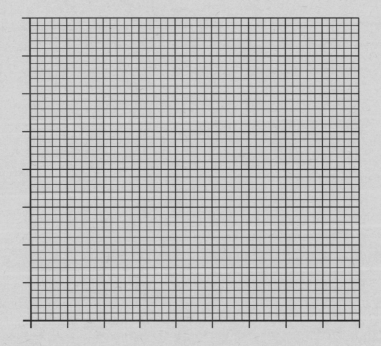

[BLANK PAGE]

FOR OFFICIAL USE

Total for
Sections B & C

X009/301

NATIONAL
QUALIFICATIONS
2005

WEDNESDAY, 18 MAY
1.00 PM – 3.30 PM

HUMAN BIOLOGY
HIGHER

Fill in these boxes and read what is printed below.

Full name of centre

Town

Forename(s)

Surname

Date of birth

Day Month Year   Scottish candidate number   Number of seat

SECTION A—Questions 1–30

Instructions for completion of Section A are given on page two.

SECTIONS B AND C

1 (a) All questions should be attempted.

(b) It should be noted that in **Section C** questions 1 and 2 each contain a choice.

2 The questions may be answered in any order but all answers are to be written in the spaces provided in this answer book, and must be written clearly and legibly in ink.

3 Additional space for answers will be found at the end of the book. If further space is required, supplementary sheets may be obtained from the invigilator and should be inserted inside the **front** cover of this book.

4 The numbers of questions must be clearly inserted with any answers written in the additional space.

5 Rough work, if any should be necessary, should be written in this book and then scored through when the fair copy has been written. If further space is required a supplementary sheet for rough work may be obtained from the invigilator.

6 Before leaving the examination room you must give this book to the invigilator. If you do not, you may lose all the marks for this paper.

SCOTTISH
QUALIFICATIONS
AUTHORITY

Read carefully

1 Check that the answer sheet provided is for **Human Biology Higher (Section A)**.

2 Check that the answer sheet you have been given has **your name**, **date of birth**, **SCN** (Scottish Candidate Number) and **Centre Name** printed on it.

   Do not change any of these details.

3 If any of this information is wrong, tell the Invigilator immediately.

4 If this information is correct, **print** your name and seat number in the boxes provided.

5 Use **black** or **blue ink** for your answers. **Do not use red ink**.

6 The answer to each question is **either** A, B, C or D. Decide what your answer is, then put a horizontal line in the space provided (see sample question below).

7 There is **only one correct** answer to each question.

8 Any rough working should be done on the question paper or the rough working sheet, **not** on your answer sheet.

9 At the end of the exam, put the **answer sheet for Section A inside the front cover of this answer book**.

Sample Question

The digestive enzyme pepsin is most active in the

A mouth

B stomach

C duodenum

D pancreas.

The correct answer is **B**—stomach. The answer **B** has been clearly marked with a horizontal line (see below).

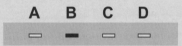

Changing an answer

If you decide to change your answer, cancel your first answer by putting a cross through it (see below) and fill in the answer you want. The answer below has been changed to **B**.

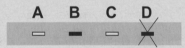

If you then decide to change back to an answer you have already scored out, put a tick (✓) to the **right** of the answer you want, as shown below:

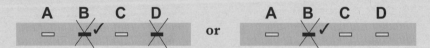

SECTION A

All questions in this section should be attempted.

Answers should be given on the separate answer sheet provided.

1. A series of enzyme-controlled reactions is shown below.

$$W \xrightarrow{\textit{enzyme 1}} X \xrightarrow{\textit{enzyme 2}} Y \xrightarrow{\textit{enzyme 3}} Z$$

   If an inhibitor which affects enzyme 2 is introduced to the system, which of the following will happen?

   A X will accumulate

   B Y will accumulate

   C X and Y will accumulate

   D Y and Z will accumulate

2. Which of the following describes metabolism correctly?

   A The breakdown of chemicals to release energy

   B The synthesis of large molecules

   C The chemical reactions of organisms

   D The breakdown of food molecules

3. The following diagram shows part of a protein molecule.

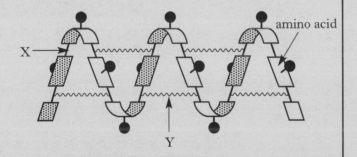

   Which line in the table describes correctly bonds X and Y?

	Bond X	Bond Y
A	hydrogen	peptide
B	hydrogen	hydrogen
C	peptide	hydrogen
D	peptide	peptide

Questions 4 and 5 refer to muscle filaments.

4. Which line of the table identifies correctly the types of filaments found in the light and dark bands of striated muscle?

	Banding pattern	
	Light	*Dark*
A	actin	myosin
B	myosin	actin + myosin
C	myosin	actin
D	actin	actin + myosin

5. When a muscle contracts what happens to these filaments?

   A Both filaments contract

   B Actin contracts but not myosin

   C Myosin contracts but not actin

   D The filaments slide over one another

6. The diagram of the cell is magnified 400 times. What is the true size of the cell?

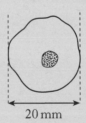

20 mm

   A $20\,\mu m$

   B $50\,\mu m$

   C $80\,\mu m$

   D $500\,\mu m$

[Turn over

7. Which of the following statements is true of all viruses?

   A They have a protein-lipid coat and contain DNA.

   B They have a protein-lipid coat and contain RNA.

   C They have a protein coat and a nucleus.

   D They have a protein coat and contain nucleic acid.

8. How many adenine molecules are present in a DNA molecule of 2000 bases, if 20% of the base molecules are cytosine?

   A 200

   B 300

   C 400

   D 600

9. In the formation of gametes, when does DNA replication occur?

   A Before the start of meiosis

   B As homologous chromosomes pair up

   C At the end of the first meiotic division

   D At the separation of chromatids

10. Alleles can be described as

   A opposite types of gamete

   B different versions of a gene

   C identical chromatids

   D non-homologous chromosomes.

11. A person has blood group AB.

    Which entry on the table identifies correctly the antigens and antibodies present?

	Antigens on cells	Antibodies in plasma
A	A and B	anti-A and anti-B
B	none	anti-A and anti-B
C	A and B	none
D	none	none

12. The gene for albinism is autosomal and recessive. A couple who are both carriers of the gene have a son. What is the chance that he will have the same genotype as his parents?

    A 1 in 1

    B 1 in 2

    C 1 in 3

    D 1 in 4

13. The family tree below shows the transmission of the Rhesus D-antigen. The gene for the Rhesus D-antigen is not sex-linked.

    ☐ Rhesus positive male

    ■ Rhesus negative male

    ○ Rhesus positive female

    ● Rhesus negative female

    Parents

    Children

    The parents are expecting a fourth child.

    What is the chance that this child will be Rhesus negative?

    A 0%

    B 25%

    C 50%

    D 100%

14. Colour blindness is a sex-linked recessive trait.

A woman would have a 50% chance of being colour blind if

A   both of her parents are carriers

B   her father has normal vision but her mother is a carrier

C   her father is a carrier and her mother is colour blind

D   her father is colour blind and her mother is a carrier.

15. Which of the following may result in the presence of an extra chromosome in the cells of a human being?

A   Non-disjunction

B   Crossing over

C   Segregation

D   Inversion

16. As an ovum develops within the ovary, it is surrounded by

A   a Graafian follicle

B   seminal fluid

C   a corpus luteum

D   the endometrium.

17. Which line in the table best describes dizygotic twins?

	Number of sperm involved in formation	Number of ova involved in formation	Resulting genotypes
A	1	1	identical
B	1	1	non-identical
C	2	2	identical
D	2	2	non-identical

18. The diagram below illustrates the hormonal control of a 30-day menstrual cycle.

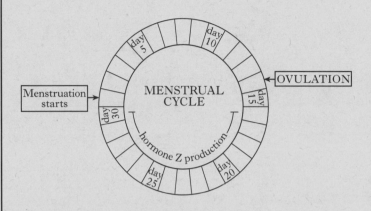

Which line of the table identifies correctly hormone Z and the structure which produces this hormone?

	Hormone Z	produced by
A	LH	ovary
B	oestrogen	corpus luteum
C	progesterone	Graafian follicle
D	progesterone	corpus luteum

19. Which of the following babies would be most likely to require a blood transfusion immediately after birth?

A   The first baby of a Rhesus negative mother and Rhesus positive father

B   The first baby of a Rhesus positive mother and Rhesus negative father

C   The second baby of a Rhesus negative mother and Rhesus positive father

D   The second baby of a Rhesus positive mother and Rhesus negative father

[Turn over

20. The diagram below shows the relationship between blood capillaries, body cells and lymph capillaries.

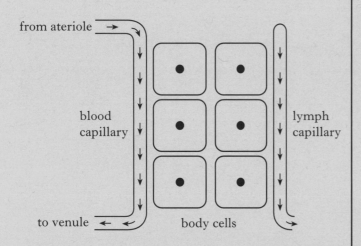

Which of the following is a correct description of the movement of oxygen to and from the body cells?

A   From body cells to blood and lymph capillaries

B   From blood capillaries to body cells

C   From lymph capillaries to body cells

D   From blood and lymph capillaries to body cells

21. If body temperature drops below normal, which of the following would result?

A   Vasodilation of skin capillaries

B   Vasoconstriction of skin capillaries

C   Decreased metabolic rate

D   Increased sweating

22. The graphs below show the average yearly increase in height of girls and boys.

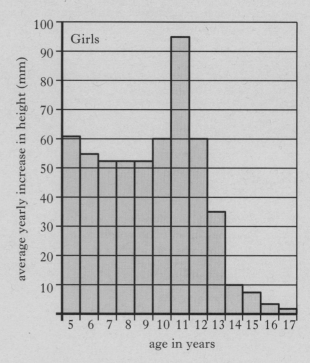

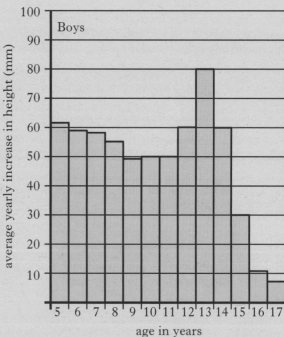

Which of the following statements is correct?

A   The greatest average yearly increase for boys occurs one year later than the greatest average yearly increase for girls.

B   Boys are still growing at seventeen but girls have stopped growing by this age.

C   Between the ages of five and eight boys grow more than girls.

D   There is no age when boys and girls show the same average yearly increase in height.

23. The diagram below shows a motor neurone.

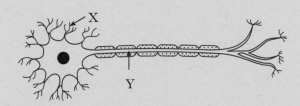

Which line of the table identifies correctly the labelled parts and the direction of impulse?

	X	Y	Direction
A	dendrite	axon	X → Y
B	dendrite	axon	Y → X
C	axon	dendrite	X → Y
D	axon	dendrite	Y → X

24. Vision in dim light is improved by the rods having

A peripheral neural pathways

B diverging neural pathways

C central neural pathways

D converging neural pathways.

25. The histogram shows the percentage distribution of IQ rating in a sample of 1000 Scottish children.

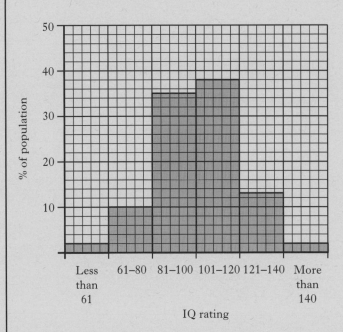

How many children have an IQ of over 120?

A 15

B 53

C 150

D 530

26. Students were asked to recall twelve letters of the alphabet in any order, after hearing the list of letters read slowly once over. An analysis of their performance is shown in the graph below.

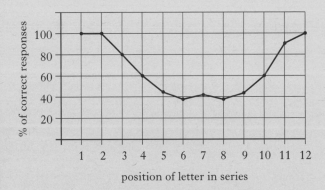

On how many occasions was a letter recalled by more than half of the students?

A 5

B 7

C 9

D 10

27. Rivers polluted by raw sewage have low oxygen concentrations as a direct result of

A   large numbers of bacteria

B   algal blooms

C   high nutrient levels

D   low nutrient levels.

28. The diagram represents part of the nitrogen cycle.

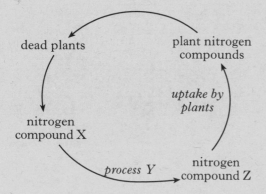

Process Y is the production of

A   ammonia by decomposition

B   nitrates by nitrification

C   ammonia by nitrogen fixation

D   nitrates by denitrification.

29. A country has a population of 10 million. What is the likely increase in population over a two-year period given a growth rate of 2% per annum?

A   102 000

B   104 040

C   204 000

D   404 000

30. The diagram below shows a population pyramid for a country.

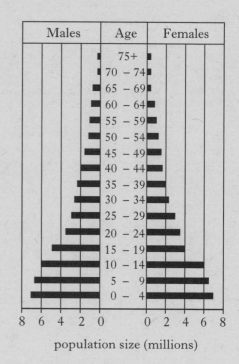

population size (millions)

How many girls between the ages of 10 and 19 are there in the population?

A   6 million

B   10 million

C   12 million

D   21 million

Candidates are reminded that the answer sheet MUST be returned INSIDE the front cover of this answer booklet.

[Turn over for Section B]

Marks

SECTION B

All questions in this section should be attempted.

1. The diagram below represents the process of RNA synthesis.

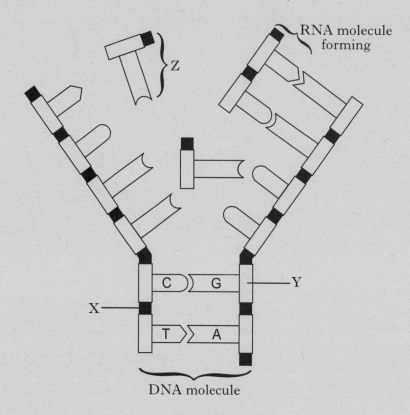

(*a*) Where in the cell does this process take place?

_____

1

(*b*) Name the components X, Y and Z.

X _____

Y _____

Z _____

2

(*c*) State the full names of any **two** different RNA bases shown in the diagram.

1 _____

2 _____

1

(*d*) Name another substance, **not** shown in the diagram, which is essential for RNA synthesis.

_____

1

Marks

1. **(continued)**

(*e*) (i) What name is given to the triplets of bases in an mRNA molecule?

_____   **1**

(ii) The table below shows some amino acids and the triplets of bases specific to them.

Amino acid	Triplet of mRNA bases
alanine	GCU
arginine	CGA
serine	UCG
histidine	CAC
valine	GUG

Name the **two** amino acids that would be specified by the mRNA molecule forming on the DNA strand in the diagram.

1 _____   2 _____   **1**

[Turn over

2. The diagram below shows three stages in the humoral immune response.

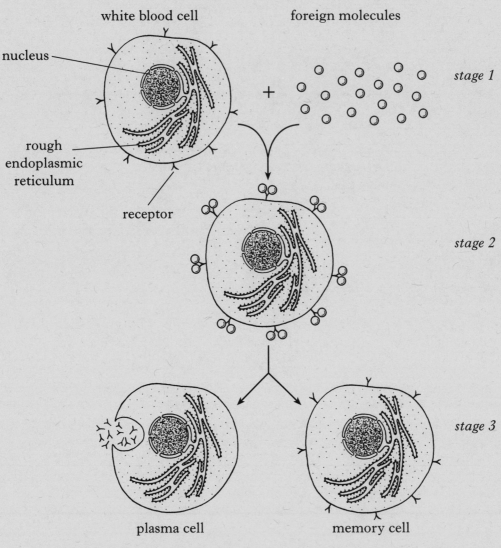

Marks

(*a*) (i) What type of white blood cell carries out the humoral immune response?

_____ 1

(ii) What name is given to foreign molecules which stimulate the immune response?

_____ 1

(*b*) Describe **two** responses made by the white blood cell as a result of the attachment of the foreign molecules.

1 _____

2 _____ 1

DO NOT WRITE IN THIS MARGIN

2. (continued) *Marks*

(*c*) Mature plasma cells contain a large quantity of rough endoplasmic reticulum. Explain this feature of these cells.

____

____

______________________________ **2**

(*d*) Suggest the role of memory cells in the immune response.

____

______________________________ **1**

(*e*) What term describes the secretion of substances, such as antibodies, out of a cell?

______________________________ **1**

(*f*) Describe how the body might obtain antibodies in a natural, passive way.

____

______________________________ **1**

[Turn over

Marks

3. The diagram below summarises a metabolic pathway within a cell.

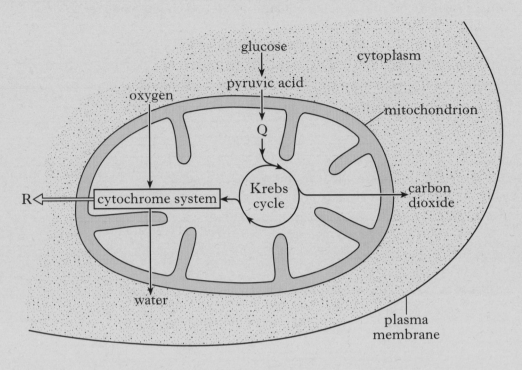

(a) Name the process which results in the formation of pyruvic acid.

_____ 1

(b) Name substance Q.

_____ 1

(c) How many carbon atoms are removed in one turn of the Krebs cycle?

_____ 1

(d) What is the role of NAD in this process?

_____ 1

(e) Why does the cytochrome system stop when oxygen is absent?

_____ 1

(f) Substance R is the main product of the cytochrome system.

Where in this metabolic pathway is substance R required?

_____ 1

Marks

4. The diagram shows sections of a testis and two seminiferous tubules.

Section A

testis

Section B

seminiferous tubules

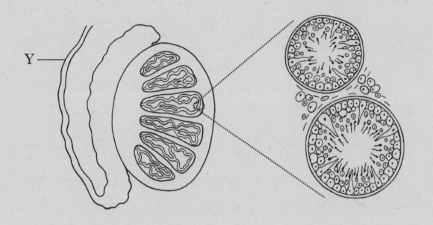

(a) Name structure Y.

_____

1

(b) Follicle stimulating hormone (FSH) affects the testes.

(i) State where FSH is produced in the body.

_____

1

(ii) What effect does FSH have on the testes?

_____

1

(c) (i) On **Section B** use an **X** to mark the site of testosterone production.

1

(ii) Describe how the concentration of testosterone in the blood is prevented from becoming too high.

_____

_____

_____

_____

2

(iii) Suggest why testosterone injections are sometimes used to treat infertility in men.

_____

_____

1

Marks

5. A nomogram is shown below. Nomograms are used to estimate the surface area of individuals.

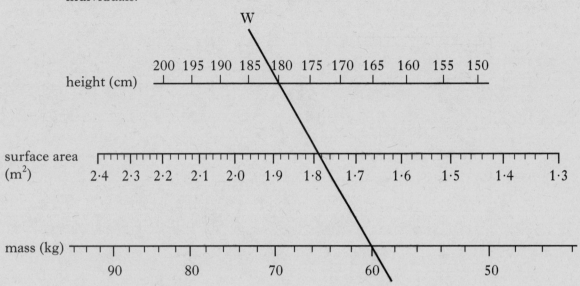

(a) The table below contains information about three individuals. Use the nomogram to complete the table. Line W has been completed as an example.

Individual	Mass (kg)	Height (cm)	Surface Area (m²)
W	60	180	1·79
X	70	160	
Y	56		1·58

1

(b) The table below shows the surface area and volume of two boys.

Name	Surface Area (m²)	Volume (dm³)
Iain	2	50
Andy	2	60

Which of these boys is likely to be more susceptible to hypothermia?

Give a reason for your answer.

Boy _____

Reason _____

_____

1

(c) Name the microscopic structures (1) in the lungs and (2) in the small intestine, which provide an increased surface area.

1 Lungs _____

2 Small intestine _____

1

Marks

6. The graph below shows the drop in pressure as blood flows through the circulatory system.

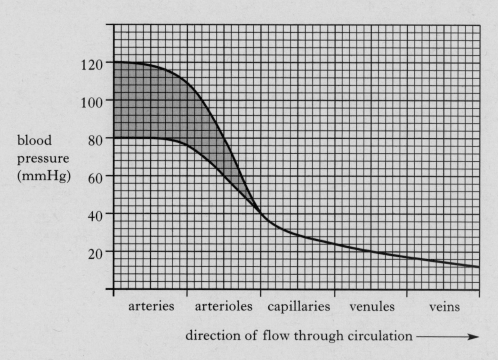

direction of flow through circulation ⟶

(a) Calculate the decrease in pressure that occurs in the capillaries.

Space for calculation

_____ mmHg   1

(b) The pressure of the blood is highest as it leaves the heart. Where in the circulation would blood be found at a pressure 25% of this value?

_____   1

(c) Why is there a maximum and minimum value given for the arteries and arterioles?

_____

_____   1

(d) Name the blood vessels which link the following organs.

1   From brain to heart _____

2   From small intestine to liver _____

3   From heart to lungs _____   2

[Turn over

Marks

7. An investigation was carried out to find out how the percentage concentration of carbon dioxide (CO_2) in inhaled air affects the volume of air breathed and the breathing rate. Ten subjects were chosen and tested at seven different concentrations of CO_2.

The graphs below show the results of this investigation.

Graph 1 Effect of CO_2 concentration on the volume of air inhaled

Graph 2 Effect of CO_2 concentration on the breathing rate

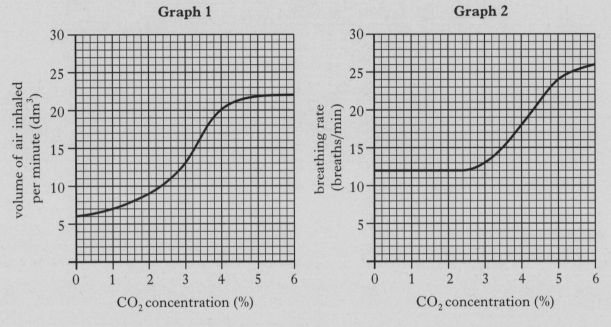

(a) From **Graph 1**, what is the volume of air inhaled in one minute when the CO_2 concentration is 3%?

_____

1

(b) From **Graph 2**, describe the effect of increasing CO_2 concentration on breathing rate.

_____

_____

_____

2

(c) (i) Complete the table below to show the mean volume of air inhaled in a single breath at each of the concentrations of CO_2 given.

CO_2 concentration of inhaled air (%)	Volume of air inhaled per minute (dm^3)	Breathing rate (breaths per minute)	Mean volume of one breath (dm^3)
0	6	12	0·50
2	9	12	
4	20		
6			

2

Marks

7. *(c)* **(continued)**

(ii) Draw a graph to show the relationship between the concentration of CO_2 in inhaled air and the mean volume of one breath.

(Additional graph paper, if required, can be found on page 32.)

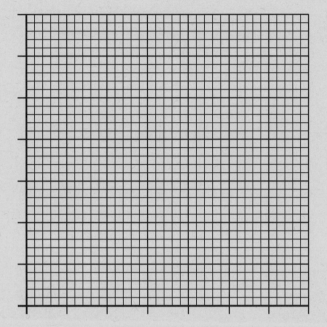

2

(iii) What conclusion can be drawn from the graph? Quote data from your graph to illustrate your answer.

_____

_____ 1

(d) (i) Before each reading was taken, each subject breathed the air samples for two minutes. Suggest a reason for this.

_____ 1

(ii) Suggest another variable, apart from time, which would have to be controlled between each reading.

_____ 1

(e) Suggest why ten subjects were chosen rather than just one.

_____

_____ 1

[Turn over

Marks

8. An investigation was carried out to determine the rates of flow and the composition of fluids in a human kidney. These were measured at positions P, Q, R and S, shown in the diagram below.

Kidney nephron

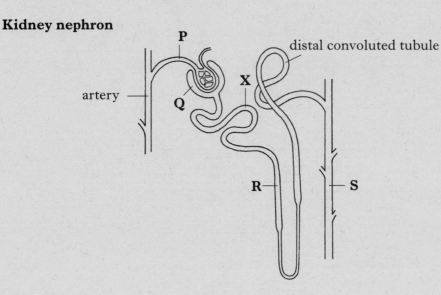

The results are given in the table below.

Position	Total flow rate through kidney (cm³/minute)	Solute concentration (g/100 cm³)		
		Protein	Glucose	Urea
P	1000	7·4	0·1	0·03
Q	100	0·0	0·1	0·03
R	20	0·0	0·0	0·15
S	1	0·0	0·0	1·85

(a) (i) Name structure **X**.

_____   1

(ii) What process takes place in this part of the nephron?

_____   1

(b) Explain why there is no protein at point **Q** in the nephron.

_____

_____   1

(c) (i) By how many times does the concentration of urea increase between points **Q** and **R**?

_____   1

Marks

8. **(c)** **(continued)**

(ii) Explain why the concentration of urea increases between points **R** and **S**.

_____

_____   1

(iii) Using data from the table, calculate the weight of urea which would pass from the collecting duct (**S**) to the bladder in one hour.

Space for calculation

_____ g   1

(d) Express the concentration of glucose at point **Q** in grams per litre.

Space for calculation

_____ g/l   1

(e) What effect would an increasing concentration of ADH in the blood have on each of the following?

(i) The concentration of urea at point **S**.

_____   1

(ii) The concentration of glucose at point **P**.

_____   1

[Turn over

Marks

9. The diagram shows the main parts of the human brain as seen in a vertical section.

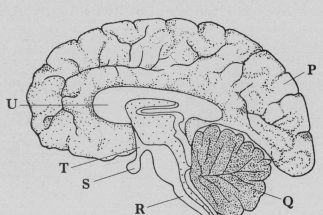

(*a*) Complete the table by adding the correct letters, names and functions of the parts.

Label	Name	Function
P		
	pituitary gland	
		temperature regulation

3

(*b*) Describe a feature of part **P** which improves its function.

_____ 1

(*c*) What is meant by the term "localisation of function"?

_____

_____ 1

(*d*) Why is the part of the brain which controls the right hand much larger than the part which controls the right foot?

_____

_____

_____ 1

Marks

10. The following diagrams represent a form of communication.

  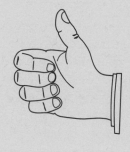

(*a*) What is this form of communication called?

_____   1

(*b*) (i) Describe the significance of such communication in infancy.

_____

_____   1

(ii) Give **two** examples of this type of communication which are used by babies.

1 _____

2 _____   1

(*c*) The following are standard symbols.

Why are such symbols used worldwide?

_____

_____   1

[Turn over

Marks

11. The account below relates to the effect of experience on behaviour.

Nicky decided she wanted to learn how to play golf. Sam, the professional, was very helpful, offering her five introductory lessons at a reasonable rate, with the offer of five more if Nicky showed consistent improvement. He emphasised that she would have to pay careful attention to his demonstrations and copy his technique.

Nicky enjoyed driving the ball but hated putting, so Sam always started lessons with putting and only moved on to using other clubs when sufficient improvement was shown. As the lessons went on, Sam expected a higher and higher standard before any driving was allowed.

Four years later Nicky was good enough to represent her country at junior level but she refused to use any of the latest graphite-shafted clubs as she had lost her first championship when using a graphite putter.

(a) With reference to the above account, give an example of each of the following types of behaviour.

Imitation _____

_____ 1

Generalisation _____

_____ 1

(b) The professional used the technique of shaping in his teaching.

What is meant by "shaping"? Give an example from the text above.

Shaping _____

_____ 1

Example _____

_____ 1

(c) As well as rewarding Nicky for doing well, Sam could also have punished any poor performance. What term is used to describe this type of training?

_____ 1

Marks

11. **(continued)**

(*d*) The paragraph below provides further information on human behaviour.

> Nicky loved playing in big championships as she found she always played better in front of a crowd. To begin with she did not like her school friends attending her big events as they, uncharacteristically, tried to distract her opponents. However, her sporting success resulted in an improvement in her friends' behaviour, and she found herself relying on their presence to raise her game.

Complete the table to identify **two** types of group or social behaviour with illustrations from the paragraph.

	Type of behaviour	*Illustration from paragraph*
1		
2		

2

[Turn over

Marks

12. The following data refer to concentrations of phosphate detected in water of Scottish rivers between 1986 and 2004.

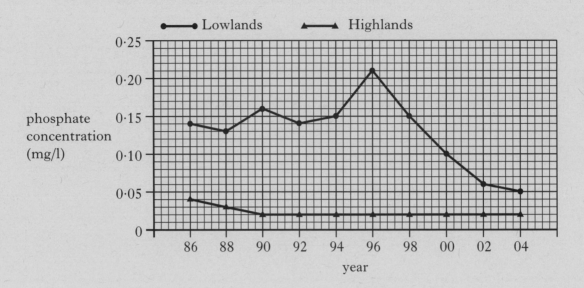

(a) What are the maximum and minimum concentrations of phosphate recorded in each of the areas?

	Phosphate Concentration (mg/l)	
Area	*Maximum*	*Minimum*
Highlands		
Lowlands		

1

(b) (i) Compare and contrast the data from 1996 to 2004.

_____

_____

_____

_____

2

(ii) Explain how the higher rainfall in the Highlands might contribute to the difference between the phosphate concentrations of rivers in the Highlands and Lowlands.

_____

_____

1

DO NOT WRITE IN THIS MARGIN

Marks

12. (*b*) (continued)

(iii) Suggest a reason for the change in phosphate concentration of the rivers in the Lowlands since 1996.

____

______________________________ **1**

(*c*) (i) Aquatic plants absorb phosphate from river water against the concentration gradient. What term is used to describe this process?

______________________________ **1**

(ii) What type of molecule in the plant cell membrane is involved in this process?

______________________________ **1**

[Turn over

Marks

SECTION C

Both questions in this section should be attempted.

Note that each question contains a choice.

Questions 1 and 2 should be attempted on the blank pages which follow.

Supplementary sheets, if required, may be obtained from the invigilator.

Labelled diagrams may be used where appropriate.

1. Answer **either** A **or** B.

   A. Describe the functions of the liver under the following headings:

   (i)   production of urea;   **2**

   (ii) metabolism of carbohydrates;   **5**

   (iii) breakdown of red blood cells.   **3**

                                                               (10)

   OR

   B. Describe the cardiac cycle under the following headings:

   (i)   nervous and hormonal control of heart beat;   **4**

   (ii) the conducting system of the heart.   **6**

                                                               (10)

In question 2 ONE mark is available for coherence and ONE mark is available for relevance.

2. Answer **either** A **or** B.

   A. Give an account of the transmission of a nerve impulse at a synapse.   **(10)**

   OR

   B. Give an account of the carbon cycle and its disruption by human activities.   **(10)**

[END OF QUESTION PAPER]

SPACE FOR ANSWERS

DO NOT
WRITE I
THIS
MARGIN

SPACE FOR ANSWERS

Page thirty

DO NOT
WRITE I
THIS
MARGIN

SPACE FOR ANSWERS

[Turn over

SPACE FOR ANSWERS

ADDITIONAL GRAPH PAPER FOR QUESTION 7(c)(ii)

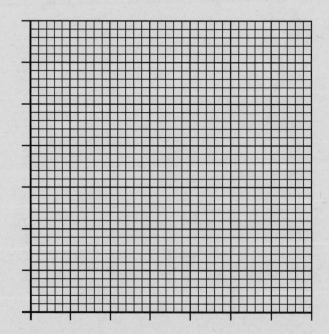

[BLANK PAGE]

FOR OFFICIAL USE

Total for
Sections B & C

X009/301

NATIONAL
QUALIFICATIONS
2006

TUESDAY, 23 MAY
1.00 PM – 3.30 PM

HUMAN BIOLOGY
HIGHER

Fill in these boxes and read what is printed below.

Full name of centre

Town

Forename(s)

Surname

Date of birth

Day   Month   Year

Scottish candidate number

Number of seat

SECTION A—Questions 1–30

Instructions for completion of Section A are given on page two.

For this section of the examination you must use an **HB pencil**.

SECTIONS B AND C

1   (a) All questions should be attempted.

(b) It should be noted that in **Section C** questions 1 and 2 each contain a choice.

2   The questions may be answered in any order but all answers are to be written in the spaces provided in this answer book, **and must be written clearly and legibly in ink**.

3   Additional space for answers will be found at the end of the book. If further space is required, supplementary sheets may be obtained from the invigilator and should be inserted inside the **front** cover of this book.

4   The numbers of questions must be clearly inserted with any answers written in the additional space.

5   Rough work, if any should be necessary, should be written in this book and then scored through when the fair copy has been written. If further space is required a supplementary sheet for rough work may be obtained from the invigilator.

6   Before leaving the examination room you must give this book to the invigilator. If you do not, you may lose all the marks for this paper.

SCOTTISH
QUALIFICATIONS
AUTHORITY

©

Read carefully

1   Check that the answer sheet provided is for **Human Biology Higher (Section A)**.

2   For this section of the examination you must use an **HB pencil**, and where necessary, an eraser.

3   Check that the answer sheet you have been given has **your name**, **date of birth**, **SCN** (Scottish Candidate Number) and **Centre Name** printed on it.

Do not change any of these details.

4   If any of this information is wrong, tell the Invigilator immediately.

5   If this information is correct, **print** your name and seat number in the boxes provided.

6   The answer to each question is **either** A, B, C or D. Decide what your answer is, then, using your pencil, put a horizontal line in the space provided (see sample question below).

7   There is **only one correct** answer to each question.

8   Any rough working should be done on the question paper or the rough working sheet, **not** on your answer sheet.

9   At the end of the exam, put the **answer sheet for Section A inside the front cover of this answer book**.

Sample Question

The digestive enzyme pepsin is most active in the

A   stomach

B   mouth

C   duodenum

D   pancreas.

The correct answer is **A**—stomach. The answer **A** has been clearly marked in **pencil** with a horizontal line (see below).

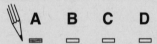

Changing an answer

If you decide to change your answer, carefully erase your first answer and, using your pencil, fill in the answer you want. The answer below has been changed to **D**.

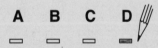

SECTION A

All questions in this section should be attempted.

Answers should be given on the separate answer sheet provided.

1. The diagram below shows a mitochondrion surrounded by cytoplasm.

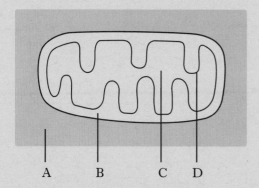

Where does glycolysis take place?

2. Which of the following statements refer to glycolysis?

   1   Carbon dioxide is released.

   2   Occurs during aerobic respiration.

   3   The end product is pyruvic acid.

   4   The end product is lactic acid.

   A   1 and 3

   B   1 and 4

   C   2 and 3

   D   2 and 4

3. In respiration, the products of the cytochrome system are

   A   hydrogen and carbon dioxide

   B   water and ATP

   C   oxygen and ADP

   D   pyruvic acid and water.

4. During anaerobic respiration in muscle fibres, what is the fate of pyruvic acid?

   A   It is converted to lactic acid.

   B   It is broken down by the mitochondria.

   C   It is broken down to carbon dioxide and water.

   D   It is converted to citric acid.

5. The table below shows the antigens and antibodies present in the four different blood groups of the ABO system.

Group	Antigen	Antibody
1	B	a
2	none	a and b
3	A and B	none
4	A	b

   Which of these groups could safely receive a transfusion of blood of group A?

   A   1 and 2

   B   1 and 4

   C   2 and 3

   D   3 and 4

6. Which of the following is a cell that engulfs bacteria?

   A   B-lymphocyte

   B   T-lymphocyte

   C   Lysosome

   D   Macrophage

7. Which of the following processes occurs during the second division of meiosis?

   A   Formation of diploid daughter cells

   B   Pairing of homologous chromosomes

   C   Separation of paired chromatids

   D   Crossing over of genetic material

8. Polygenic characteristics are different from monohybrid characteristics because they

   A   show random assortment of chromosomes

   B   show independent assortment of chromosomes

   C   are controlled by many pairs of alleles

   D   are caused by non-disjunction during meiosis.

9. The gene (m) which causes one type of muscular dystrophy is sex-linked and recessive to the normal gene (M). If a carrier female and an unaffected male have children, what would be the predicted effect on their sons and daughters?

	Sons	Daughters
A	100% are affected	100% are carriers
B	50% are affected	50% are carriers
C	50% are affected	100% are carriers
D	100% are affected	50% are carriers

10. Red-green colour deficient vision is a sex-linked condition. John, who is affected, has the family tree shown below.

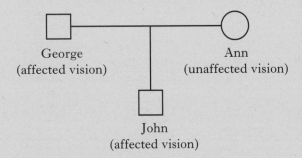

George
(affected vision)

Ann
(unaffected vision)

John
(affected vision)

If b is the mutant allele for the condition, which of the following could be the genotypes of George's parents and Ann's parents?

	George's parents		Ann's parents	
A	X^BX^b	X^BY	X^BX^B	X^BY
B	X^BX^B	X^bY	X^BX^B	X^BY
C	X^BX^b	X^BY	X^BX^b	X^BY
D	X^BX^B	X^bY	X^BX^B	X^bY

11. After ovulation, the follicle develops into the

A corpus luteum

B fallopian tube

C endometrium

D zygote.

12. Which of the following best describes monozygotic twins?

A They are genetically similar and have developed from two eggs fertilised by two sperm.

B They are genetically similar and have developed from one egg fertilised by two sperm.

C They are genetically identical and have developed from one egg fertilised by one sperm.

D They are genetically identical and have developed from one egg fertilised by two sperm.

13. Which of the following sequences describes the first stages in the development of an embryo?

A fertilisation → cleavage → implantation

B implantation → fertilisation → cleavage

C cleavage → fertilisation → implantation

D fertilisation → implantation → cleavage

14. Which of the following hormones is produced by the placenta?

A Growth hormone

B Prolactin

C Progesterone

D Oxytocin

15. The graph shows changes in lung volume during a breathing exercise.

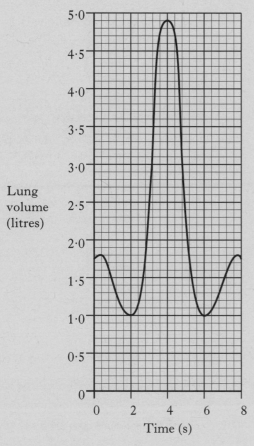

Lung volume (litres)

Time (s)

What is the volume of air exhaled between 4 and 6 seconds?

A   3·8 litres

B   3·9 litres

C   4·8 litres

D   4·9 litres

16. Which of the following structures is **not** involved in the production or breakdown of red blood cells?

A   Spleen

B   Pancreas

C   Liver

D   Bone marrow

17. The diagram shows a cross-section of the heart.

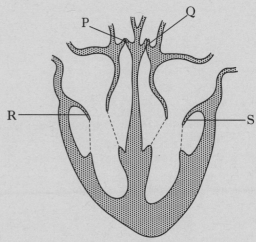

Which of the following describes correctly the movement of the valves during ventricular systole?

A   Valves P and Q open and valves R and S close

B   Valves P and R open and valves Q and S close

C   Valves P and Q close and valves R and S open

D   Valves P and R close and valves Q and S open

18. The trace below was obtained from a patient who was having the electrical activity of his heart monitored.

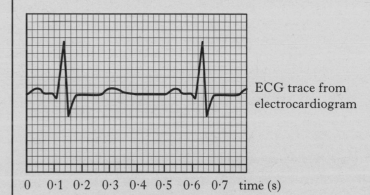

ECG trace from electrocardiogram

time (s)

What was the heart rate of this patient?

A   42 beats per minute

B   72 beats per minute

C   86 beats per minute

D   120 beats per minute

19. The graph below shows how pulse rate and stroke volume change with the rate of oxygen uptake.

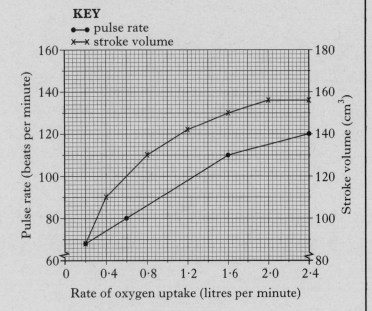

KEY
- ●—● pulse rate
- ×—× stroke volume

Cardiac output = pulse rate × stroke volume

What is the cardiac output when the oxygen uptake is 1·6 litres per minute?

A   13·1 litres per minute

B   14·3 litres per minute

C   16·5 litres per minute

D   16·9 litres per minute

20. In a healthy human, blood entering the kidney contains more glucose than blood leaving the kidney because the glucose is

A   changed to waste by the kidney tubules

B   stored by the kidney cells

C   excreted by the kidney tubules

D   used by the kidney cells for respiration.

21. The concentration of urea rises from $0·03 \, g/100 \, cm^3$ to $0·15 \, g/100 \, cm^3$ as it passes through a kidney tubule.

What is the difference in concentration, expressed as a whole number ratio?

A   1 : 5

B   1 : 50

C   3 : 100

D   2 : 1

22. When body temperature rises, which of the following is true of blood flow in the skin capillaries?

A   The flow of blood in the capillaries increases and heat loss decreases.

B   The flow of blood in the capillaries increases and heat loss increases.

C   The flow of blood in the capillaries decreases and heat loss decreases.

D   The flow of blood in the capillaries decreases and heat loss increases.

23. In which part of the brain are the control centres for both speech and hearing located?

A   Limbic system

B   Hypothalamus

C   Medulla oblongata

D   Cerebrum

24. The function of the corpus callosum is to

A   transfer information from a sensory nerve to a motor nerve

B   control balance and coordination

C   transfer information from one hemisphere to the other

D   control all sensory activities.

25. In which of the following is part of the autonomic nervous system correctly linked to the response it causes?

	Part of the autonomic nervous system	*Response*
A	sympathetic	acceleration of heart beat
B	sympathetic	vasodilation of skin arterioles
C	parasympathetic	secretion of sweat
D	parasympathetic	vasodilation of coronary blood vessels

26. When a person's beliefs are changed as a result of persuasion, this is an example of

A   internalisation

B   identification

C   deindividuation

D   social facilitation.

27. The graph below contains information about fertiliser usage.

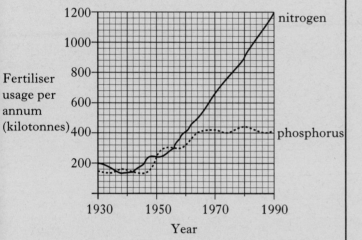

Which of the following statements about nitrogen usage between 1930 and 1990 is correct?

A   It increased steadily.

B   It increased by 500%.

C   It increased by 600%.

D   It always exceeded phosphorus usage.

28. The bar chart below shows the percentage loss in yield of four organically grown crops as a result of the effects of weeds, disease and insects.

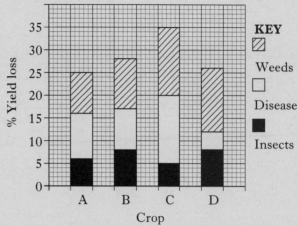

Predict which crop is most likely to show the greatest increase in yield if herbicides and insecticides were applied.

[Turn over

29. The graph below contains information about the birth rate and death rate in Mexico.

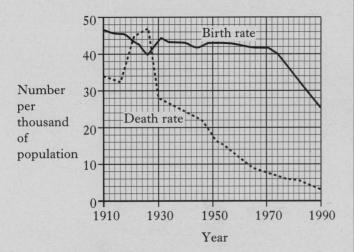

Which of the following conclusions can be drawn from the graph?

A   At no time during the century has the population of Mexico decreased.

B   The greatest increase in population occurred in 1970.

C   The population was growing faster in 1910 than in 1990.

D   Birth rate decreased between 1970 and 1990 due to the use of contraception.

30. The diagram below shows the carbon cycle.

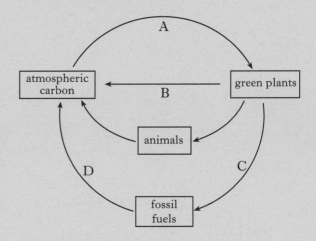

Which letter represents combustion?

Candidates are reminded that the answer sheet MUST be returned INSIDE the front cover of this answer booklet.

Marks

SECTION B

All questions in this section should be attempted.

All answers must be written clearly and legibly in ink.

1. (*a*) The diagram below shows a structural model of the plasma membrane.

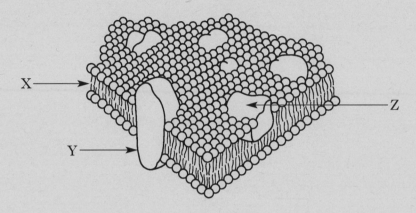

(i) What term describes this model of the membrane?

_____ 1

(ii) Identify components X and Y.

X _____

Y _____ 1

(iii) State a possible function of Z.

_____ 1

(*b*) Sodium ions can be moved against a concentration gradient across a membrane.

(i) Explain what is meant by a concentration gradient across a membrane.

_____

_____ 1

(ii) What term describes the movement of ions against a concentration gradient?

_____ 1

(iii) Explain why a shortage of oxygen might lead to a decrease in the rate of sodium ion movement.

_____

_____

_____ 2

2. (*a*) Complete the table below to show the mRNA codons and tRNA anticodons for each amino acid.

Marks

Amino acid	mRNA codons	tRNA anticodons
alanine		CGA
threonine	ACC	
cysteine		ACA

1

(*b*) The diagram shows the primary structure of part of a protein molecule.

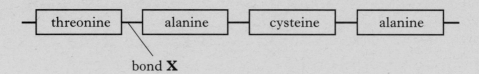

bond **X**

(i) Use the information from the table above to determine the DNA base sequence which would code for this molecule.

_____

1

(ii) Name bond **X**.

_____

1

(iii) Describe **one** way in which the secondary structure of a protein differs from the primary structure.

_____

_____

_____

_____

1

(*c*) Where in the cell are proteins packaged and prepared immediately before secretion?

_____

1

Marks

3. The diagram shows a polio virus.

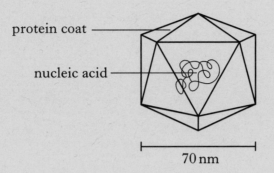

protein coat ——————

nucleic acid ——————

├———— 70 nm ————┤

(a) Viruses can only reproduce within a host cell.

    (i) List **two** substances, supplied by the host cell, which are required for viral replication.

       1 _____

       2 _____   1

    (ii) What happens after the viruses have been assembled inside the cell?

       _____

       _____

       _____   1

(b) Viruses can be processed to make vaccines to protect against the disease.

Suggest why it is important that the nucleic acid is damaged in the process, but not the protein coat.

Nucleic acid damaged _____

_____

_____   1

Protein coat undamaged _____

_____

_____   1

(c) The average diameter of a red blood cell is 7 µm.

By how many times is a red blood cell bigger than a polio virus? (1 µm = 1000 nm)

Space for calculation

_____   1

4. Polydactyly is an inherited condition in which individuals are born with extra toes. The allele for polydactyly is dominant and not sex-linked.

The family tree below shows the incidence of the condition through three generations.

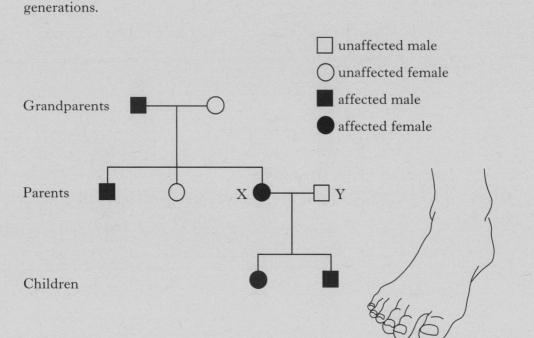

□ unaffected male

○ unaffected female

■ affected male

● affected female

Grandparents

Parents

X   Y

Children

Marks

(*a*) (i) Using the symbol **D** for the allele for polydactyly and **d** for the normal allele, give the genotypes of the two children.

_____ and _____

1

(ii) Individuals X and Y are expecting another child.

What are the chances of this child inheriting the condition?

_____

1

(*b*) (i) What evidence from the family tree confirms that the grandfather is heterozygous?

_____

_____

1

(ii) What evidence from the family tree confirms that the condition is not sex-linked?

_____

_____

1

(*c*) What term is used to refer to chromosomes which are not sex-chromosomes?

_____

1

Marks

5. The diagrams show the hormonal control of the testes and ovaries by the pituitary gland.

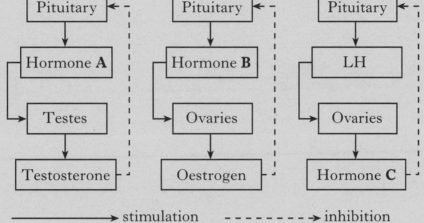

⟶ stimulation   - - - - - - -→ inhibition

(a) (i) What name is given to this type of hormonal control?

_____   1

(ii) Identify hormones **A**, **B** and **C**.

A _____

B _____

C _____   2

(iii) State an effect of oestrogen on the pituitary gland, other than that shown above.

_____   1

(iv) Where in the testes is testosterone produced?

_____   1

(b) Distinguish between cyclical fertility and continuous fertility.

_____

_____

_____   1

(c) The female contraceptive pill raises the levels of ovarian hormones in the blood. Explain why this has a contraceptive effect.

_____

_____

_____   2

6. The diagram shows the blood supply between a fetus and its placenta.

Marks

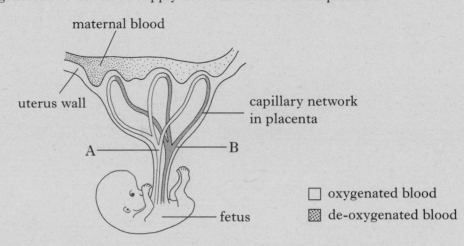

maternal blood

uterus wall

capillary network
in placenta

A ——————— B

☐ oxygenated blood
▨ de-oxygenated blood

fetus

(a) Name **two** waste products that pass from the fetal blood to the maternal blood.

1 _____ 2 _____

1

(b) The table shows some substances and their method of exchange between the fetal and maternal blood. Complete the table.

Substance	Method of exchange
	diffusion
glucose	
antibodies	

2

(c) Which of the fetal blood vessels, A or B, is the artery?
Give a reason for your answer.

Vessel _____

Reason for answer _____

_____

1

(d) Why might the second Rhesus positive child of a Rhesus negative mother be in danger from the mother's immune system?

_____

_____

_____

_____

2

(e) Why do some inborn errors of metabolism, such as phenylketonuria (PKU), only have an effect on the baby *after* birth?

_____

_____

_____

1

Marks

7. The diagram shows the liver and its associated blood supply.

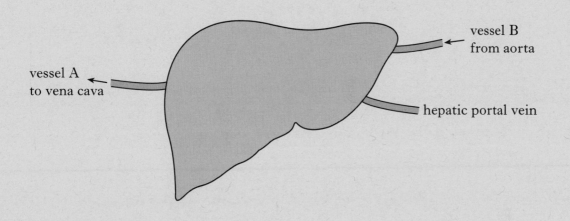

vessel B
from aorta

vessel A
to vena cava

hepatic portal vein

(*a*)　(i)　Identify the vessels labelled A and B.

A _____　　B _____　　**1**

(ii)　Name an organ which is linked to the liver by the hepatic portal vein.

_____　　**1**

(*b*)　The table below relates to products of digestion, their vessel of transportation in the villus and their possible fate in the body.

Complete the table.

Product of digestion	*Vessel of transportation*	*Possible fate*
glucose		
		deamination in the liver
	lacteal	

3

(*c*)　Identify **two** hormones which cause the liver to release glucose, and state the conditions under which each of the hormones is released.

1　Hormone _____

　　Condition _____　　**1**

2　Hormone _____

　　Condition _____　　**1**

[Turn over

Marks

8. A student carried out an investigation into the effectiveness of thermal insulation.

Two flasks containing water at 50 °C were left for forty minutes. During this time the temperature of the water was recorded every ten minutes. The results are given in the table below.

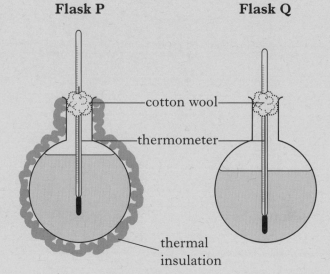

	Temperature (°C)	
Time (min)	Flask P	Flask Q
0	50	50
10	44	37
20	39	30
30	36	24
40	34	20

(a) Present the data in a suitable form on the graph paper.

(Additional graph paper, if required, can be found on page 28.)

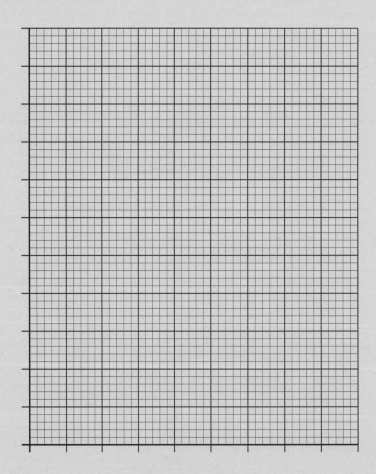

3

Marks

8. **(continued)**

(*b*) Calculate the percentage decrease in temperature in flasks P and Q over the 40-minute period.

P_____ %   Q _____ %   **1**

(*c*) The student concluded that the insulation had slowed the cooling rate of the flask.

Describe **two** aspects of the experimental design which make his conclusion invalid.

1 _____

_____

2 _____

_____   **1**

(*d*) Another student went on to compare flasks of different sizes without any insulation. She compared a $50 \, cm^3$ flask with a $100 \, cm^3$ flask, each completely filled with hot water.

(i) State **two** variables that would have to be kept the same during this second investigation.

1 _____

2 _____   **1**

(ii) Which flask would cool more quickly? Give a reason for your answer.

Flask _____

Reason _____

_____

_____   **1**

(*e*) What part of the brain monitors body temperature?

_____   **1**

[Turn over

Marks

9. The diagram shows a neuromuscular synapse.

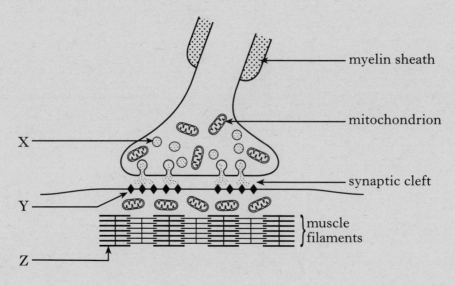

myelin sheath

mitochondrion

synaptic cleft

X

Y

muscle filaments

Z

(*a*) (i) Name cell structure **X**.

_____

1

(ii) Describe the role of structure **X** in exocytosis.

_____

_____

1

(*b*) What is the function of molecule **Y**?

_____

_____

1

(*c*) The areas on both sides of the synaptic cleft are rich in mitochondria. Explain why mitochondria are needed in each area.

_____

_____

_____

2

(*d*) (i) Name protein filament **Z**.

_____

1

(ii) Describe what happens to the length of this filament when the muscle contracts.

_____

1

Marks

10. An investigation was carried out to study the serial position effect.
Twelve pictures were shown, one by one, to five children.
The children were then asked to recall the pictures they saw.
The results of the investigation are shown below.
The table shows the recall success for each picture.

Child	Position of picture in list shown to children											
	1st	2nd	3rd	4th	5th	6th	7th	8th	9th	10th	11th	12th
1	✓	✓	✓	✓	✗	✗	✓	✗	✓	✓	✓	✓
2	✓	✓	✓	✗	✗	✓	✗	✗	✓	✗	✓	✓
3	✓	✗	✓	✓	✗	✗	✗	✗	✗	✓	✓	✗
4	✓	✓	✗	✗	✗	✗	✓	✓	✓	✓	✓	✓
5	✓	✓	✓	✗	✓	✗	✗	✓	✗	✓	✓	✓
Recall (%)	100	80	80	40	20	20	40	40	60	80	100	80

✓ = picture recalled   ✗ = picture forgotten

(a) (i) Describe the trend shown by these results.

_____

_____

_____   1

(ii) Explain these results in terms of the serial position effect.

_____

_____

_____

_____

_____

_____

_____

_____

_____   3

(b) To make sure that the children tried their best, the investigation was designed
as a competition and the child with the best recall was rewarded.

What behavioural term describes improved performance in competitive
situations?

_____   1

Marks

11. Analysis of fertility rates can be used to predict population change over the next hundred years.

Graph 1 shows the number of children born to a sample of twenty UK women of reproductive age. The sample was taken in the year 2000.

Graph 1

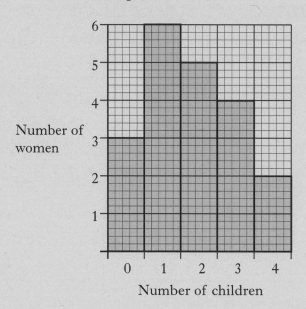

Number of
women

Number of children

(a) The fertility rate for a country is calculated by dividing the total number of children by the number of women in the sample.

  (i) From **Graph 1**, calculate the fertility rate of this UK sample.

  _____   1

  (ii) How could the calculation of the UK fertility rate be made more reliable?

  _____

  _____

  _____   1

  (iii) The age of each woman is not given. Why might this information be important?

  _____

  _____

  _____   1

Marks

11. **(continued)**

Graph 2 shows the predicted population changes in the UK for four different fertility rates.

Graph 2

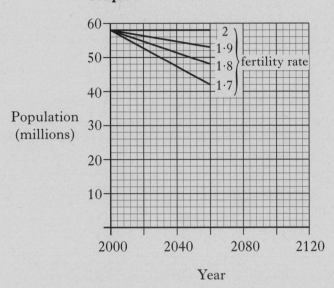

(*b*) Using the fertility rate you calculated from **Graph 1**, predict the population of the UK in the year 2100.

_____

1

(*c*) In a sample of twenty families in Thailand, a developing country, three women have two children, ten women have three children and seven women have four children.

(i) What is the fertility rate for this sample?

Space for calculation

_____ 1

(ii) Suggest a reason for the difference in fertility rate between Thailand and the UK.

_____

_____ 1

(*d*) Birth rates and death rates can also be used to predict population changes. Give **one** other factor which would affect the size of a population.

_____ 1

(*e*) What term is used to describe studies of population statistics such as this?

_____ 1

Marks

12. The tables below contain information about the population of the United Kingdom in the year 2000.

Table 1 – Populations of individual countries

Country	Population (millions)
England	48·9
Scotland	4·9
Wales	2·7
Nothern Ireland	1·5
Total	**58·0**

Table 2 – Population profile of UK

Group	Numbers (millions)
Under 16 years	11·6
16–59 years	34·4
60 years and over	12·0
Males	28·0
Females	30·0

(a) From **Table 1**, calculate the percentage of the UK population that is Scottish.

Space for calculation

—————— %   1

(b) From **Table 2**, calculate the male to female sex ratio.

Space for calculation

————— : —————   1
male   female

(c) Use the information in **Tables 1** and **2** to estimate the number of children under sixteen years of age, living in Scotland.

Space for calculation

——————   1

Marks

13. The diagram below shows three possible fates of nitrates which have been added to the soil as fertiliser.

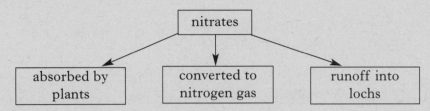

(a) Why are nitrates essential for plant growth?

_____   1

(b) What type of bacteria convert nitrate to nitrogen gas?

_____   1

(c) Explain how the runoff of nitrates into a loch ecosystem might result in a drop in the oxygen concentration of the water.

_____

_____

_____

_____

_____

_____   2

(d) Describe **two** ways by which the nitrate content of the soil can increase naturally.

1 _____

_____

2 _____

_____   1

[Turn over for SECTION C on *Page twenty-four*

Marks

SECTION C

Both questions in this section should be attempted.

Note that each question contains a choice.

Questions 1 and 2 should be attempted on the blank pages which follow.

Supplementary sheets, if required, may be obtained from the invigilator.

Labelled diagrams may be used where appropriate.

1. Answer **either** A **or** B.

   A. Give an account of respiration under the following headings:

      (i) the role of ATP within the cell;   **4**

      (ii) the use of different respiratory substrates.   **6**

                               (10)

   OR

   B. Give an account of enzymes under the following headings:

      (i) factors affecting enzyme activity;   **7**

      (ii) activation of enzymes.   **3**

                               (10)

In question 2, ONE mark is available for coherence and ONE mark is available for relevance.

2. Answer **either** A **or** B.

   A. Describe the effect of experience on learning.   **(10)**

   OR

   B. Discuss the impact of an increasing population on the world's water supplies.   **(10)**

[END OF QUESTION PAPER]

SPACE FOR ANSWERS

SPACE FOR ANSWERS

Page twenty-six

SPACE FOR ANSWERS

[Turn over

DO NOT
WRITE I
THIS
MARGIN

SPACE FOR ANSWERS

ADDITIONAL GRAPH PAPER FOR QUESTION 8(a)

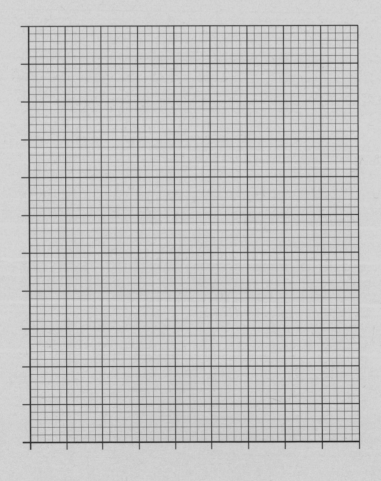

[BLANK PAGE]

FOR OFFICIAL USE

Total for
Sections B & C

X009/301

NATIONAL
QUALIFICATIONS
2007

MONDAY, 21 MAY
1.00 PM – 3.30 PM

HUMAN BIOLOGY
HIGHER

Fill in these boxes and read what is printed below.

Full name of centre

Town

Forename(s)

Surname

Date of birth
Day Month Year   Scottish candidate number   Number of seat

SECTION A—Questions 1–30

Instructions for completion of Section A are given on page two.

For this section of the examination you must use an **HB pencil**.

SECTIONS B AND C

1   (a) All questions should be attempted.

(b) It should be noted that in **Section C** questions 1 and 2 each contain a choice.

2   The questions may be answered in any order but all answers are to be written in the spaces provided in this answer book, **and must be written clearly and legibly in ink**.

3   Additional space for answers will be found at the end of the book. If further space is required, supplementary sheets may be obtained from the invigilator and should be inserted inside the **front** cover of this book.

4   The numbers of questions must be clearly inserted with any answers written in the additional space.

5   Rough work, if any should be necessary, should be written in this book and then scored through when the fair copy has been written. If further space is required a supplementary sheet for rough work may be obtained from the invigilator.

6   Before leaving the examination room you must give this book to the invigilator. If you do not, you may lose all the marks for this paper.

SCOTTISH
QUALIFICATIONS
AUTHORITY

LI X009/301 6/8270

Read carefully

1 Check that the answer sheet provided is for **Human Biology Higher (Section A)**.

2 For this section of the examination you must use an **HB pencil** and, where necessary, an eraser.

3 Check that the answer sheet you have been given has **your name**, **date of birth**, **SCN** (Scottish Candidate Number) and **Centre Name** printed on it.

   Do not change any of these details.

4 If any of this information is wrong, tell the Invigilator immediately.

5 If this information is correct, **print** your name and seat number in the boxes provided.

6 The answer to each question is **either** A, B, C or D. Decide what your answer is, then, using your pencil, put a horizontal line in the space provided (see sample question below).

7 There is **only one correct** answer to each question.

8 Any rough working should be done on the question paper or the rough working sheet, **not** on your answer sheet.

9 At the end of the exam, put the **answer sheet for Section A inside the front cover of this answer book**.

Sample Question

The digestive enzyme pepsin is most active in the

A   stomach

B   mouth

C   duodenum

D   pancreas.

The correct answer is **A**—stomach. The answer **A** has been clearly marked in **pencil** with a horizontal line (see below).

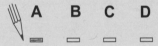

Changing an answer

If you decide to change your answer, carefully erase your first answer and, using your pencil, fill in the answer you want. The answer below has been changed to **D**.

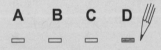

SECTION A

All questions in this section should be attempted.

Answers should be given on the separate answer sheet provided.

1. Which line in the table correctly identifies the two cell structures shown in the diagram?

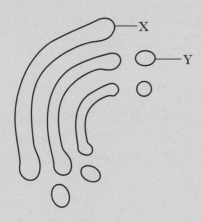

	X	Y
A	Endoplasmic reticulum	Vesicle
B	Endoplasmic reticulum	Ribosome
C	Golgi body	Vesicle
D	Golgi body	Ribosome

2. Which of the following correctly describes metabolism?

   A The breakdown of chemicals to release energy

   B The rate at which an organism produces heat energy

   C The chemical reactions of organisms

   D The breakdown of food molecules

3. Phenylketonuria (PKU) is a metabolic disorder which can be lethal in childhood. It is caused by an inability to make *enzyme X*, shown in the metabolic pathway below.

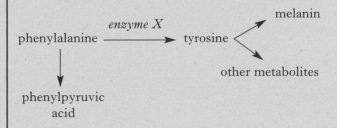

   Which substance would have to be removed from the diet for someone who has this disorder?

   A Phenylalanine

   B Enzyme X

   C Tyrosine

   D Melanin

4. A stock solution has a concentration of 1 M. $100\,cm^3$ of a 0·4 M solution can be prepared by adding

   A $40\,cm^3$ of stock solution to $60\,cm^3$ of water

   B $60\,cm^3$ of stock solution to $40\,cm^3$ of water

   C $40\,cm^3$ of stock solution to $100\,cm^3$ of water

   D $100\,cm^3$ of stock solution to $40\,cm^3$ of water.

5. Non-competitive inhibitors affect enzyme action by

   A acting as a co-enzyme for enzyme action

   B altering the shape of the substrate molecule

   C competing for the active site of the enzyme

   D altering the shape of the active site of the enzyme.

[Turn over

6. The graph shows the effect of substrate concentration on the rate of an enzyme-catalysed reaction.

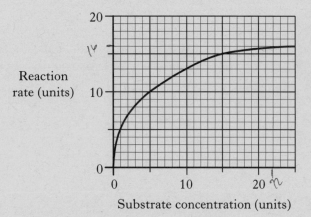

Reaction rate (units)

Substrate concentration (units)

At what substrate concentration is the reaction rate equal to 75% of the maximum rate?

A   6 units

B   8 units

C   12 units

D   18 units

7. Which of the following is **not** a protein?

A   Actin

B   Insulin

C   Amylase

D   Ribonucleic acid

8. The phospholipid molecules in a cell membrane allow the

A   free passage of glucose molecules

B   self-recognition of cells

C   active transport of ions

D   membrane to be fluid.

9. Red blood cells have a solute concentration of around 0·9%.

Which of the following statements correctly describes the fate of these cells when immersed in a 1% salt solution?

A   The cells will burst.

B   The cells will shrink.

C   The cells will expand but not burst.

D   The cells will remain unaffected.

10. The secretion of amylase from a cell is an example of

A   endocytosis

B   exocytosis

C   pinocytosis

D   phagocytosis.

11. Lymphocytes act in the defence of the body by

A   ingesting toxins

B   ingesting pathogens

C   producing lysosomes

D   producing antibodies.

12. The graphs below show the effect of two injections of an antigen on the formation of an antibody.

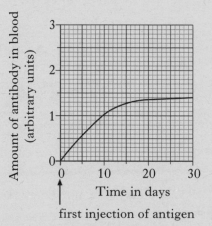

first injection of antigen

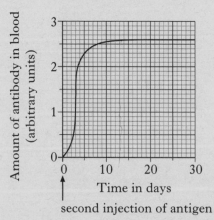

second injection of antigen

How many days after the second injection does the amount of antibody in the blood reach the maximum achieved after the first injection?

A   3 days

B   6 days

C   20 days

D   30 days

13. Haploid gametes are produced during meiosis as a result of

A the separation of homologous chromosomes

B the independent assortment of chromosomes

C the separation of chromosomes into chromatids

D the crossing over of chromatids.

14. The diagram refers to human reproduction.

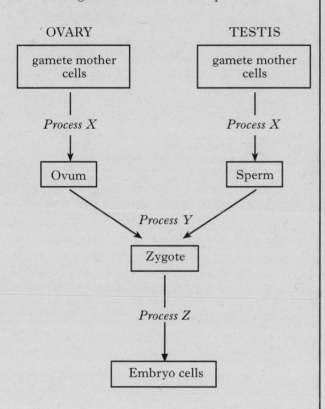

Which of the following correctly identifies processes X, Y and Z?

	X	Y	Z
A	mitosis	meiosis	fertilisation
B	meiosis	fertilisation	mitosis
C	meiosis	mitosis	fertilisation
D	mitosis	fertilisation	meiosis

15. The family tree shows the pattern of inheritance of a genetic condition.

Unaffected female × Unaffected male

↓

Affected female

The allele responsible for this condition is both

A sex-linked and recessive

B sex-linked and dominant

C autosomal and recessive

D autosomal and dominant.

16. Non-disjunction can be described as

A a metabolic disorder

B a type of antisocial behaviour

C a condition resulting in memory loss

D a form of chromosome mutation.

17. Which of the following organs monitors body temperature?

A Hypothalamus

B Pituitary gland

C Prostate gland

D Spleen

18. Which line of the table correctly identifies the function and site of production of bile salts?

	Function	Site of production
A	digest protein	liver
B	digest protein	gall bladder
C	emulsify fats	liver
D	emulsify fats	gall bladder

[Turn over

19. Which of the following vessels in the circulatory system contains blood at the lowest pressure?

    A   Jugular vein

    B   Renal vein

    C   Vena cava

    D   Hepatic portal vein

20. The following data refer to the breathing of an athlete (a) resting and (b) just after a race.

	Breathing rate (breaths per minute)	Volume of one breath	Carbon dioxide in exhaled air (%)
(a) Resting	10	500 ml	5
(b) After race	22	1 litre	5

Assuming the rate of breathing remains constant, what would be the volume of carbon dioxide breathed out during the first two minutes after the race?

    A   1·1 litres

    B   2·2 litres

    C   22 litres

    D   44 litres

21. The table shows the masses of various substances in the glomerular filtrate and in the urine over a period of 24 hours.

Which of the substances has the smallest percentage reabsorption from the glomerular filtrate?

	Substance	Mass in glomerular filtrate (g)	Mass in urine (g)
A	Sodium	600·0	6·0
B	Potassium	35·0	2·0
C	Uric acid	8·5	0·8
D	Calcium	5·0	0·2

22. Which of the following shows the direction of a nerve impulse in a neurone?

    A   Axon → cell body → dendrite

    B   Cell body → dendrite → axon

    C   Cell body → axon → dendrite

    D   Dendrite → cell body → axon

23. The diagram below shows the ages (in months) at which children reach various stages in their development.

The left end of each bar indicates the age by which 25% of infants have reached the stated performance.

The right end of each bar indicates the age by which 90% of infants have reached the stated performance.

The vertical bar indicates the age by which 50% of infants have reached the stated performance.

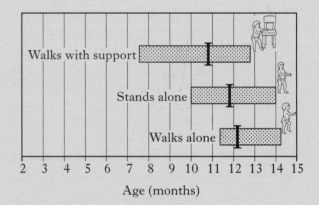

Age (months)

An eight-month old infant can walk with support but cannot stand alone.

In what percentage of the population is this child found?

    A   Less than 25%

    B   Between 25% and 50%

    C   Around 50%

    D   Between 50% and 90%

24. Identical twins are valuable in the study of behaviour because

    A   genetic and environmental factors can be discounted

    B   maturation and environmental factors can be discounted

    C   genetic factors can be discounted

    D   genetic, maturation and environmental factors can be discounted.

25. Which of the following terms describes the process by which a person learns to distinguish between different but related stimuli?

 A   Generalisation

 B   Imitation

 C   Discrimination

 D   Identification

26. An investigation was carried out to determine how long it takes students to learn to run a finger maze. A blindfolded student was allowed to run the maze on ten occasions. The results are given in the table below.

Trial	Time (s)
1	23
2	20
3	26
4	12
5	18
6	10
7	6
8	7
9	6
10	6

How could the investigation be improved to make the results more reliable?

 A   Allow other students to try to run the maze ten times, whilst blindfolded

 B   Allow the same student some additional trials on the same maze

 C   Change the shape of the maze and allow the same student to repeat ten trials

 D   Record the times to one decimal place

27. Which of the following is a correct definition of demography?

 A   Calculation of the difference between birth rates and death rates

 B   A count of the number of individuals in a population

 C   The rate at which a population replaces itself

 D   The study of population numbers

28. Which of the following processes increases directly the concentration of nitrogen gas in the atmosphere?

 A   Decomposition

 B   Denitrification

 C   Detoxification

 D   Deamination

29. The diagram below shows part of the nitrogen cycle.

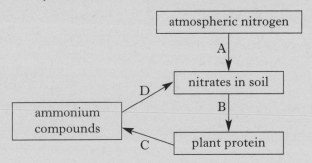

Which letter represents nitrogen fixation?

30. Over-application of which of the following substances on agricultural land is likely to induce algal blooms in adjacent lakes?

 A   Fertiliser

 B   Insecticide

 C   Fungicide

 D   Herbicide

Candidates are reminded that the answer sheet MUST be returned INSIDE the front cover of this answer booklet.

[Turn over for Section B

[BLANK PAGE]

DO NOT
WRITE IN
THIS
MARGIN

Marks

SECTION B

All questions in this section should be attempted.

All answers must be written clearly and legibly in ink.

1. The diagram below shows part of a DNA molecule.

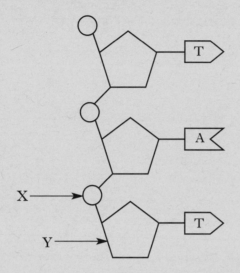

(*a*)   (i)   On the diagram, draw a circle around **one** nucleotide.   1

(ii)   Name parts X and Y.

X _____

Y _____   1

(*b*)   Name the **two** DNA bases **not** shown in the diagram.

_____ and _____   1

(*c*)   (i)   State the mRNA codon which would be formed from the triplet of DNA bases shown.

_____   1

(ii)   Apart from nucleotides, name another molecule needed for the synthesis of mRNA.

_____   1

(*d*)   A DNA molecule was found to contain 15 000 nucleotides.

What is the maximum number of amino acids which could be coded for by this molecule?

_____   1

[Turn over

DO NOT
WRITE I
THIS
MARGIN

Marks

2. The diagram below shows three stages that occur during aerobic respiration.

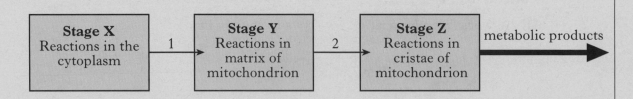

(a) Name each stage.

X _____

Y _____

Z _____   2

(b) (i) Arrows 1 and 2 represent the transfer of molecules from one stage to another. Complete the table to identify these molecules.

Arrow	Name of molecule
1	
2	

2

(ii) Name the **two** metabolic products of stage Z.

_____ and _____   1

(c) The diagram below shows a mitochondrion from a skin cell.

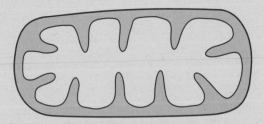

Describe how the structure of a mitochondrion from an active muscle cell would differ from the one shown. Give a reason for your answer.

Structural difference _____

_____   1

Reason _____

_____   1

Marks

3. The family tree shows the inheritance of a bone disorder.

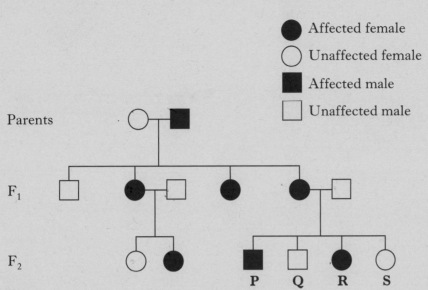

● Affected female

○ Unaffected female

■ Affected male

□ Unaffected male

Parents

F_1

F_2

P   Q   R   S

The disorder is caused by a dominant sex-linked allele (**B**).

(a) Using appropriate symbols, give the genotypes of individuals **P, Q, R** and **S**.

P_____ **Q**_____ **R**_____ **S**_____   2

(b) (i) Explain why all the F_1 females in this family are affected.

_____

_____

_____   1

(ii) Explain why only some of the F_2 females in this family are affected.

_____

_____

_____   1

(c) Is the ratio of affected offspring to unaffected offspring in the F_1 generation as expected? Give a reason for your answer.

Yes/No _____

Reason _____

_____   1

Marks

4. The diagrams below show a disease-causing virus and one of the same type which has been weakened to make it less harmful.

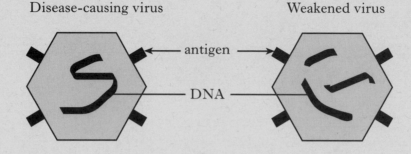

Disease-causing virus   Weakened virus

antigen

DNA

(a) A woman is vaccinated with the weakened form of the virus.

(i) Explain why she does not develop the disease from the vaccination.

_____

_____ 1

(ii) What feature of the weakened virus results in her gaining immunity from the disease?

_____

_____ 1

(iii) Explain why this form of immunity is described as being both artificial and active.

Artificial _____

_____ 1

Active _____

_____ 1

(b) The table contains information about viruses.

Tick (✓) the appropriate boxes to show characteristics which apply to all viruses.

Characteristic	Tick (✓)
Contains a nucleus	
Surrounded by a protein coat	
Can be seen under a light microscope	
Contains nucleic acid	
Can only reproduce inside other cells	

2

Marks

5. (*a*) The diagrams below contain information about three hormones involved in the control of milk production.

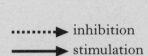

Placenta

Hormone X ┊ ┊ Hormone Y

Pituitary Gland

Pituitary Gland

Hormone Z

Mammary Glands manufacture milk

┈┈┈▶ inhibition

━━━▶ stimulation

(i) Names hormones X, Y and Z.

X _____

Y _____

Z _____　　　　2

(ii) Placental hormones inhibit the production of hormone Z by the pituitary gland. With reference to the diagrams, explain why milk production starts after birth.

_____

_____

_____　　2

(*b*) (i) What name is given to the first milk produced by the mammary glands?

_____　　1

(ii) State **one** difference in the content of this first milk compared with breast milk which is produced later.

_____　　1

(*c*) Complete the following table which contains information about hormones produced by the pituitary gland.

Name of hormone	Target organ	Effect of hormone on target organ
ADH	kidney	
	testes	testosterone production
oxytocin		muscular contraction

2

Marks

6. The graph below shows the occurrence of high blood pressure in British men of different ages.

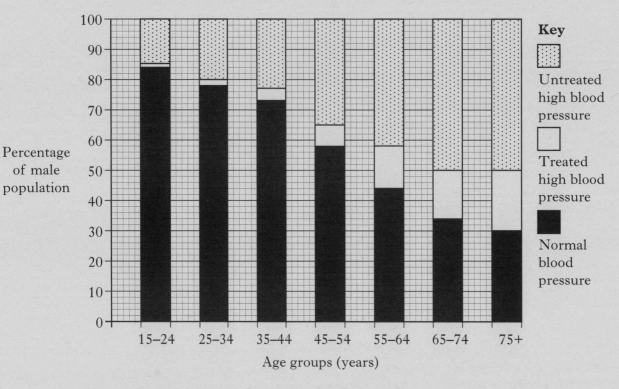

Key

- Untreated high blood pressure
- Treated high blood pressure
- Normal blood pressure

Percentage of male population — Age groups (years)

(*a*) (i) What percentage of British men aged between 25 and 34 have high blood pressure?

_____

1

(ii) In men aged 55–64 who have high blood pressure, what is the percentage of treated to untreated individuals expressed as a simple ratio?

Space for working

_____ : _____   1
  treated   untreated

(iii) Describe **one** trend shown by the graph and suggest an explanation for it.

Trend _____   1

Explanation _____

_____

_____   1

DO NOT WRITE IN THIS MARGIN

Marks

6. (continued)

(*b*) A blood pressure reading that is greater than 160/90 mmHg is regarded as being too high.

Why are blood pressure readings given as two figures?

1

(*c*) Beta-blockers are drugs often used in the treatment of high blood pressure.

(i) Beta-blockers cause vasodilation. Explain how this lowers blood pressure.

1

(ii) Beta-blockers also slow heart rate. Suggest which region of the heart is likely to be affected by beta-blockers.

1

[Turn over

Marks

7. The diagram below shows the liver, intestine and associated blood vessels.

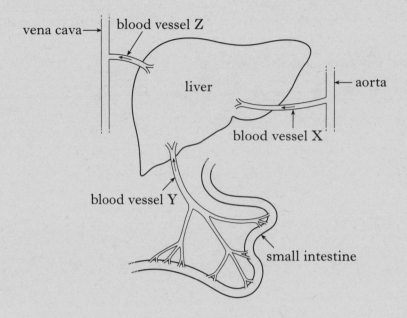

vena cava → | blood vessel Z

liver

← aorta

blood vessel X

blood vessel Y

small intestine

(a) (i) Identify blood vessels X, Y and Z.

X _____

Y _____

Z _____

2

(ii) Describe the differences in oxygen and carbon dioxide concentrations between blood vessel X and blood vessel Z.

_____

_____

_____

1

(b) (i) Glucose is absorbed into the blood stream from the small intestine.

Describe **two** ways in which the small intestine is designed to maximise glucose absorption.

1 _____

_____

2 _____

_____

1

Marks

7. **(*b*)** **(continued)**

(ii) Describe **two** possible fates of the absorbed glucose when it reaches the liver.

1 _____

_____

2 _____

_____   **1**

(*c*) The liver metabolises a large number of substances.

(i) Name a substance excreted from the liver when red blood cells are broken down.

_____   **1**

(ii) What compounds are broken down in the liver to produce urea?

_____   **1**

[Turn over

Page seventeen

Marks

8. The graphs below contain information about the regulation of blood sugar.

Graph 1 shows how the concentration of glucose in the blood affects the concentration of insulin.

Graph 2 shows how the concentration of insulin in the blood affects the rate of glucose uptake by the liver.

Graph 1

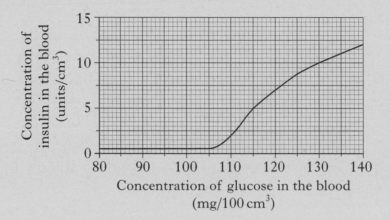

Graph 2

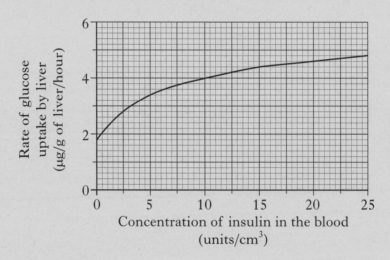

(*a*) (i) From **Graph 1**, state the glucose concentration which triggers an increase in insulin production.

_____ 1

(ii) Name the organ which produces insulin.

_____ 1

(*b*) From **Graph 2**, calculate the percentage increase in the rate of glucose uptake by the liver when the concentration of insulin in the blood rises from 10 to 15 units/cm³.

Space for calculation

_____ 1

(*c*) From **Graphs 1** and **2**, state the rate of glucose uptake by the liver when the concentration of glucose in the blood is 130 mg/100 cm³.

_____ μg/g of liver/hour 1

Official SQA Past Papers: Higher Human Biology 2007

DO NOT
WRITE IN
THIS
MARGIN

Marks

9. The diagram shows a section through part of the central nervous system.

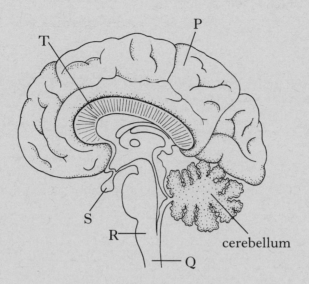

(a) The table contains information about three parts of the central nervous system. Complete the table to identify the parts and their functions.

Label	Name	Function
		Controls voluntary actions
T		Links left and right side of brain
	Spinal cord	

3

(b) Complete the following sentences by <u>underlining</u> one option from each pair of options shown in **bold**.

The parasympathetic nervous system is part of the **autonomic / somatic**

nervous system which originates in the **medulla / cerebellum**.

Parasympathetic nerves **speed up / slow down** heart rate.

1

(c) What structural feature of motor and sensory neurones speeds up the transmission of nerve impulses?

_____

_____

1

[Turn over

Marks

10. An investigation was carried out to find out how an infant's play was affected by the presence or absence of an adult. The infant was tested at three-month intervals using the following procedure.

1   The infant was placed in a room with an adult and some toys.
2   The infant was allowed to play with the toys for five minutes, then the adult left the room.
3   The infant was allowed to continue to play with the toys for another five minutes alone.

Playing time was measured by the number of seconds the infant spent playing per minute.

The graph shows the change in time spent playing, at each age, after the adult left the room.

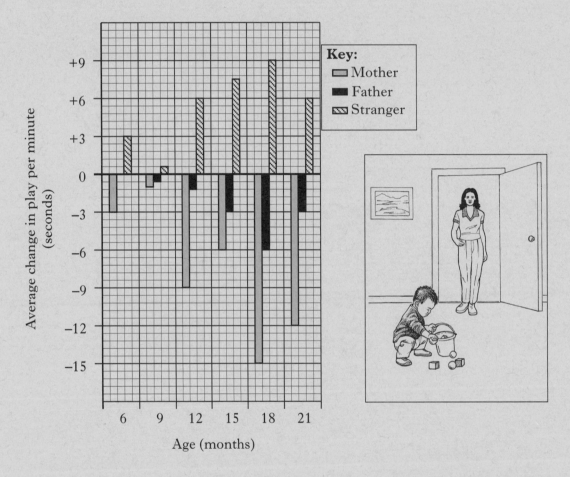

(a) At what ages does the departure of any adult have the **greatest** and **least** effect on the length of play time?

Greatest effect _____ months   Least effect _____ months   1

(b) When the child was 21 months old, what was the total increase in playing time, over the 5-minute period, when the stranger left the room?

_____ seconds   1

DO NOT WRITE IN THIS MARGIN

Marks

10. (continued)

(*c*) (i) Compare the effect of the departure of the mother with the departure of the father. **1**

(ii) Suggest a reason for this difference. **1**

(*d*) (i) Compare the effect of the departure of the stranger with the departure of the parents. **1**

(ii) Suggest reasons for this difference. **2**

(*e*) How could the reliability of this investigation be improved? **1**

[Turn over

DO NOT
WRITE
THIS
MARGI

Marks

11. An investigation was carried out on the effect of strobe lighting and loud noise on the ability of students to perform calculations.

Twenty students were divided into two equal groups, A and B. Each group was given 20 calculations to complete.

Group A sat in an evenly lit, quiet room.
Group B sat in a room where there was strobe lighting and loud noise.

The numbers of errors the students made, while doing the calculations, are shown in **Table 1**.

Table 1

Group A		Group B	
Student	Number of errors	Student	Number of errors
1	2	1	8
2	4	2	5
3	3	3	9
4	1	4	4
5	3	5	6
6	0	6	3
7	2	7	4
8	3	8	7
9	1	9	6
10	1	10	8

(*a*) By how many times has the average number of errors increased as a result of the distractions?

Space for calculation

_____ 1

(*b*) State **three** factors which would need to be kept constant during this investigation.

1 _____

2 _____

3 _____ 2

DO NOT
WRITE IN
THIS
MARGIN

Marks

11. (continued)

(c) A third group of ten students carried out the investigation under the same conditions as group B, but were tested six times instead of only once. Each test comprised different calculations. The average percentage of errors is shown in **Table 2**.

Table 2

Trial	1	2	3	4	5	6
Average percentage error	34	30	24	20	20	19

(i) Construct a line graph to show the data in the table.

(Additional graph paper, if required, can be found on page 32.)

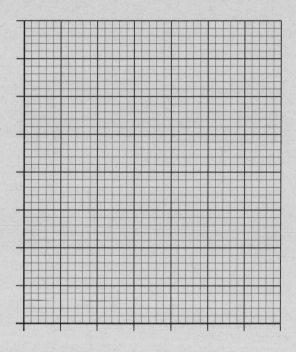

2

(ii) Suggest an explanation for the shape of the graph.

_____

_____ 1

(d) How could the design of the investigation be altered to demonstrate the effect of social facilitation?

_____

_____

_____ 1

12. **Graph A** shows how the average global temperature, between 1860 and 2000, varied from that in 1970.

Graph A

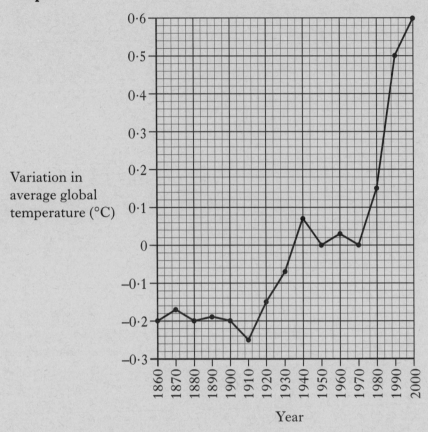

Graph B shows the global fossil fuel consumption, between 1860 and 2000.

Graph B

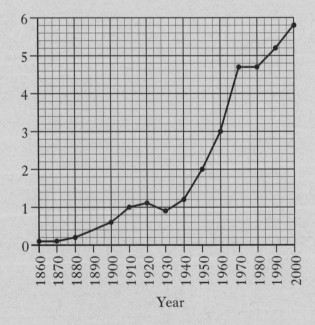

DO NOT
WRITE IN
THIS
MARGIN

Marks

12. (continued)

(a) What was the increase in average global temperature between 1900 and 2000?

_____

1

(b) State **two** reasons for the increased use of fossil fuels.

1 _____

2 _____   **1**

(c) Discuss the extent to which the graphs support the theory that rising global temperatures are due to increasing use of fossil fuels.

Quote data from the graph in your answer.

_____

_____

_____

_____

_____

_____

_____

_____   **2**

(d) Name a greenhouse gas other than carbon dioxide.

_____

1

[Turn over

13. The photograph below shows the effect of deforestation on an area of tropical rainforest.

Marks

(*a*)   (i)   State **two** reasons why humans remove forest from the land.

1 _____

_____

2 _____

_____   **2**

     (ii)   Deforestation can result in desertification. Explain how this can happen.

_____

_____

_____

_____

_____   **2**

(*b*)   Describe **one** other effect of deforestation on the local environment.

_____

_____

_____   **1**

Marks

SECTION C

Both questions in this section should be attempted.

Note that each question contains a choice.

Questions 1 and 2 should be attempted on the blank pages which follow.

Supplementary sheets, if required, may be obtained from the invigilator.

Labelled diagrams may be used where appropriate.

1. Answer **either** A **or** B.

   A. Give an account of the function of a synapse under the following headings:

   (i) release of neurotransmitter;   3

   (ii) action of neurotransmitter;   3

   (iii) removal of neurotransmitter.   4

   OR   **(10)**

   B. Give an account of memory under the following headings:

   (i) encoding into short-term memory;   2

   (ii) transfer from short-term to long-term memory;   6

   (iii) retrieval from long-term memory.   2

                                                                                 (10)

In question 2, ONE mark is available for coherence and ONE mark is available for relevance.

2. Answer **either** A **or** B.

   A. Give an account of the causes and treatment of female infertility.   **(10)**

   OR

   B. Give an account of how the structure of a red blood cell relates to its function.   **(10)**

[END OF QUESTION PAPER]

DO NOT
WRITE IN
THIS
MARGIN

SPACE FOR ANSWERS

SPACE FOR ANSWERS

SPACE FOR ANSWERS

SPACE FOR ANSWERS

[Turn over

SPACE FOR ANSWERS

ADDITIONAL GRAPH PAPER FOR QUESTION 11(c)(i)

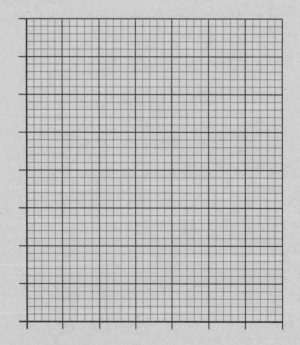

[BLANK PAGE]

FOR OFFICIAL USE

Total for
Sections B & C

X009/301

NATIONAL
QUALIFICATIONS
2008

TUESDAY, 27 MAY
1.00 PM – 3.30 PM

HUMAN BIOLOGY
HIGHER

Fill in these boxes and read what is printed below.

Full name of centre

Town

Forename(s)

Surname

Date of birth

Day Month Year   Scottish candidate number   Number of seat

SECTION A—Questions 1–30

Instructions for completion of Section A are given on page two.

For this section of the examination you must use an **HB pencil**.

SECTIONS B AND C

1 (a) All questions should be attempted.

   (b) It should be noted that in **Section C** questions 1 and 2 each contain a choice.

2 The questions may be answered in any order but all answers are to be written in the spaces provided in this answer book, **and must be written clearly and legibly in ink**.

3 Additional space for answers will be found at the end of the book. If further space is required, supplementary sheets may be obtained from the invigilator and should be inserted inside the **front** cover of this book.

4 The numbers of questions must be clearly inserted with any answers written in the additional space.

5 Rough work, if any should be necessary, should be written in this book and then scored through when the fair copy has been written. If further space is required a supplementary sheet for rough work may be obtained from the invigilator.

6 Before leaving the examination room you must give this book to the invigilator. If you do not, you may lose all the marks for this paper.

Read carefully

1 Check that the answer sheet provided is for **Human Biology Higher (Section A)**.

2 For this section of the examination you must use an **HB pencil**, and where necessary, an eraser.

3 Check that the answer sheet you have been given has **your name**, **date of birth**, **SCN** (Scottish Candidate Number) and **Centre Name** printed on it.

Do not change any of these details.

4 If any of this information is wrong, tell the Invigilator immediately.

5 If this information is correct, **print** your name and seat number in the boxes provided.

6 The answer to each question is **either** A, B, C or D. Decide what your answer is, then, using your pencil, put a horizontal line in the space provided (see sample question below).

7 There is **only one correct** answer to each question.

8 Any rough working should be done on the question paper or the rough working sheet, **not** on your answer sheet.

9 At the end of the exam, put the **answer sheet for Section A inside the front cover of this answer book**.

Sample Question

The digestive enzyme pepsin is most active in the

A stomach

B mouth

C duodenum

D pancreas.

The correct answer is **A**—stomach. The answer **A** has been clearly marked in **pencil** with a horizontal line (see below).

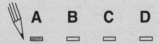

Changing an answer

If you decide to change your answer, carefully erase your first answer and, using your pencil, fill in the answer you want. The answer below has been changed to **D**.

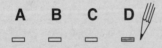

SECTION A

All questions in this section should be attempted.

Answers should be given on the separate answer sheet provided.

1. During which of the following chemical conversions is ATP produced?

   A   Amino acids ⟶ protein

   B   Glucose ⟶ pyruvic acid

   C   Haemoglobin ⟶ oxyhaemoglobin

   D   Nucleotides ⟶ mRNA

2. The following statements relate to respiration and the mitochondrion.

   1   Glycolysis takes place in the mitochondrion.

   2   The mitochondrion has two membranes.

   3   The rate of respiration is affected by temperature.

   Which of the above statements are correct?

   A   1 and 2

   B   1 and 3

   C   2 and 3

   D   All of them

3. The anaerobic breakdown of glucose splits from the aerobic pathway of respiration

   A   after the formation of pyruvic acid

   B   after the formation of acetyl CoA

   C   after the formation of citric acid

   D   at the start of glycolysis.

4. In respiration, the products of the cytochrome system are

   A   hydrogen and carbon dioxide

   B   water and ATP

   C   oxygen and ADP

   D   pyruvic acid and water.

5. The key below can be used to identify carbohydrates.

   1   Soluble...................................... 2
       Insoluble................................... glycogen

   2   Benedict's test positive 3
       Benedict's test negative .... sucrose

   3   Barfoed's test positive 4
       Barfoed's test negative .... lactose

   4   Clinistix test positive .... glucose
       Clinistix test negative .... fructose

   Which line in the table of results below is **not** in agreement with the information contained in the key?

	Carbohydrate	Benedict's test	Barfoed's test	Clinistix test
A	lactose	positive	negative	not tested
B	glucose	positive	negative	positive
C	fructose	positive	positive	negative
D	sucrose	negative	not tested	not tested

6. Which of the following is an immune response?

   A   T-lymphocytes secreting antigens

   B   T-lymphocytes carrying out phagocytosis

   C   B-lymphocytes combining with foreign antigens

   D   B-lymphocytes producing antibodies

7. Phagocytes contain many lysosomes so that

   A   enzymes which destroy bacteria can be stored

   B   toxins from bacteria are neutralised

   C   antibodies can be released in response to antigens

   D   bacteria can be engulfed into the cytoplasm.

8. Which of the following is an example of active immunity?

   A   Antibody production following exposure to antigens

   B   Antibodies crossing the placenta from mother to fetus

   C   Antibodies passing from the mother's milk to a suckling baby

   D   Antibody extraction from one mammal to inject into another

9. The following steps occur during the replication of a virus.

   1   Alteration of host's cell metabolism

   2   Production of viral protein coats

   3   Replication of viral DNA

   In which sequence do these events occur?

   A   1 ⟶ 3 ⟶ 2

   B   1 ⟶ 2 ⟶ 3

   C   2 ⟶ 1 ⟶ 3

   D   3 ⟶ 1 ⟶ 2

10. The diagram below shows a stage in meiosis.

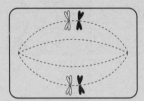

   Which of the following diagrams shows the next stage in meiosis?

   A 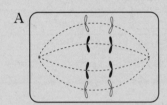   B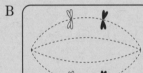

   C 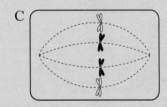   D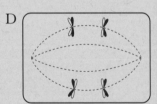

11. Cystic fibrosis is a genetic condition caused by an allele which is not sex-linked.

   A child is born with cystic fibrosis despite neither parent having the condition.

   The parents are going to have a second child. What is the chance this child will have cystic fibrosis?

   A   75%

   B   67%

   C   50%

   D   25%

12. A sex-linked condition in humans is caused by a recessive allele. What is the chance of an unaffected man and a carrier woman having an unaffected male child?

   A   1 in 1

   B   1 in 2

   C   1 in 3

   D   1 in 4

13. One function of the seminal vesicles is to

   A   produce testosterone

   B   allow sperm to mature

   C   store sperm temporarily

   D   produce nutrients for sperm.

14. Which fertility treatment would be appropriate for a woman with blocked uterine tubes?

   A   Provision of fertility drugs

   B   *In vitro* fertilisation

   C   Artificial insemination

   D   Calculation of fertile period

15. A 30 g serving of breakfast cereal contains 1·5 mg of iron. Only 25% of this iron is absorbed into the bloodstream.

   If a pregnant woman requires 6 mg of iron per day, how much cereal would she have to eat each day to meet this requirement?

   A   60 g

   B   120 g

   C   240 g

   D   480 g

16. Which of the following blood vessels carries oxygenated blood?

   A   Renal vein

   B   Hepatic vein

   C   Pulmonary vein

   D   Hepatic portal vein

17. In which of the following situations might a fetus be at risk from Rhesus antibodies produced by the mother?

	Father	Mother
A	Rhesus positive	Rhesus negative
B	Rhesus positive	Rhesus positive
C	Rhesus negative	Rhesus negative
D	Rhesus negative	Rhesus positive

18. The diagram below shows an ECG trace taken during exercise.

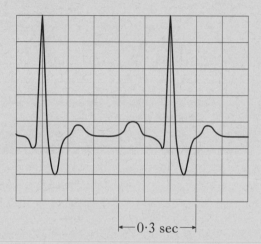

The person's heart rate is

A   80 bpm

B   100 bpm

C   120 bpm

D   140 bpm.

19. The diagram below shows a section through the human heart.

What is the correct position of the pacemaker?

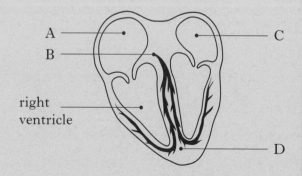

20. The vessel by which blood leaves the liver is the

A   renal vein

B   hepatic portal vein

C   renal artery

D   hepatic vein.

21. The graph below shows an individual's skin temperature and rate of sweat production over a period of 50 minutes.

Key

——— sweat production

------ skin temperature

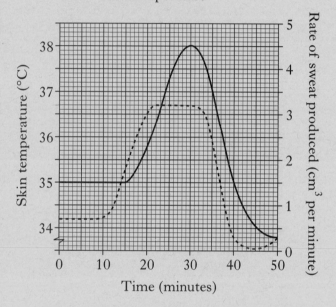

What is the skin temperature when the rate of sweat production is at a maximum?

A   3·2 °C

B   4·5 °C

C   36·7 °C

D   38·0 °C

[Turn over

22. The following diagram represents four neurones in a neural pathway.

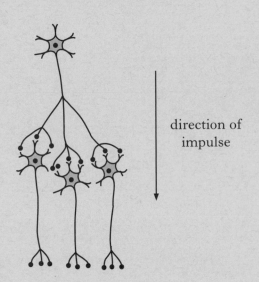

direction of impulse

Which line in the table describes the pathway correctly?

	Type of pathway	
A	motor	divergent
B	motor	convergent
C	sensory	divergent
D	sensory	convergent

23. Which of the following carries an impulse towards a nerve cell body?

A   Dendrite

B   Axon

C   Myelin

D   Myosin

24. Which of the following statements describes a neurotransmitter and its method of removal?

A   Adrenaline is removed by reabsorption.

B   Adrenaline is removed by enzyme degradation.

C   Noradrenaline is removed by enzyme degradation.

D   Noradrenaline is removed by reabsorption.

25. The diagram below illustrates the relationship between short and long-term memory.

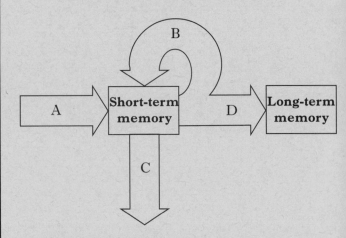

Which arrow represents the process of rehearsal?

26. The behavioural term *generalisation* is defined correctly as the ability to

A   make appropriate different responses to different but related stimuli

B   make the same appropriate response to different but related stimuli

C   submerge one's personal identity in the anonymity of a group

D   improve performance in competitive situations.

27. The table below contains information about the populations of four countries in the year 2000.

In which country did the population decrease?

	Number per 1000 inhabitants			
Country	Births	Deaths	Immigrants	Emigrants
A	9·3	10·1	1·0	0·1
B	9·7	10·3	1·3	0·4
C	10·1	9·9	0·2	0·5
D	10·8	10·5	0·1	0·3

28. The diagram below shows the number of people dying from different causes in a developing country. (Figures are in millions.)

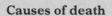

Causes of death

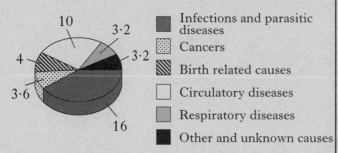

What percentage of deaths is due to birth related causes?

A   4%

B   8%

C   10%

D   11%

29. Which of the following processes is carried out by bacteria found in root nodules?

A   Denitrification

B   Nitrification

C   Nitrogen fixation

D   Deamination

30. Which of the following does **not** play a part in global warming?

A   The cutting down of forests

B   Methane production by cattle

C   The increase in use of motor vehicles

D   The increased use of fertilisers on farmland

Candidates are reminded that the answer sheet MUST be returned INSIDE the front cover of this answer booklet.

[Turn over for Section B

Marks

SECTION B

All questions in this section should be attempted.

All answers must be written clearly and legibly in ink.

1. The diagram below illustrates the two main stages of protein synthesis.

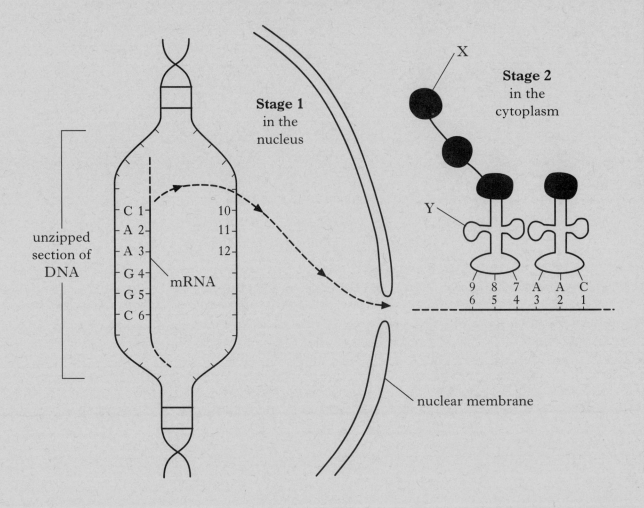

(a) Describe **three** differences between DNA and mRNA.

1 _____

_____

2 _____

_____

3 _____

_____   2

Marks

1. **(continued)**

(*b*) Name bases 3, 8 and 11.

Base 3 _____

Base 8 _____

Base 11 _____   2

(*c*) **Circle** a codon in the diagram opposite.   1

(*d*) Where in the cytoplasm does stage 2 take place?

_____   1

(*e*) Name molecules X and Y.

X _____   Y _____   1

(*f*) The newly synthesised protein may be secreted from the cell.

(i) Name the cell structure where the protein would be found just before it enters a secretory vesicle.

_____   1

(ii) Describe what happens to the protein while it is in this cell structure.

_____   1

[Turn over

2. (*a*) The diagram below shows some of the functions of proteins in the cell membrane.

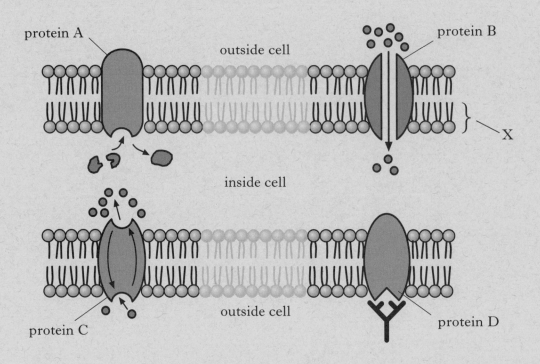

    (i)   Use the information from the diagram to complete the table below.

Protein	Function
	Transports molecules by diffusion
A	
D	
	Transports molecules by active transport

    (ii)   Identify molecule X and describe its function within the membrane.

        Molecule X _____

        Function _____

        _____

  (*b*) Describe what happens to the cell membrane during the process of endocytosis.

    _____

    _____

    _____

Marks

3

2

2

Marks

3. The blood group of an individual is controlled by three alleles *A*, *B* and *O*.

Alleles *A* and *B* are co-dominant and completely dominant to allele *O*.

The diagram below shows the blood groups of three generations of a family.

Parents　　Mother　　　　　　　　　　　　　Father
　　　　　　　Group B　　　　　　　　　　　　Group A

Children　　Son 1　　　　　Son 2　　　　　Daughter ——— Husband
　　　　　　　Group A　　　　Group O　　　　　　　　　　 Group O

Grandchildren　　　　　　　　　　　Grandson　　　　Granddaughter
　　　　　　　　　　　　　　　　　　Group B　　　　　Group A

(a) What is the blood group of the daughter?

　—————　　　　　　　　　　　　　　　　　　　　　　　　　1

(b) State the genotypes of the grandchildren.

　Grandson　——————　　　　　Granddaughter　——————　　　1

(c) How many of the three children are homozygous?

　—————　　　　　　　　　　　　　　　　　　　　　　　　　1

(d) Explain the meaning of the term *co-dominant*.

　_____

　_____　1

(e) Only one of the sons can safely receive a blood transfusion from his brother.
Indicate whether this statement is true or false and explain your decision.

　True/False　_____

　Explanation　_____

　_____

　_____

　_____　2

[Turn over

4. The graphs below show the plasma concentrations of certain hormones throughout a woman's menstrual cycle.

Graph 1 shows the concentrations of FSH and LH.

Graph 2 shows the concentration of two other hormones, X and Y.

Graph 1

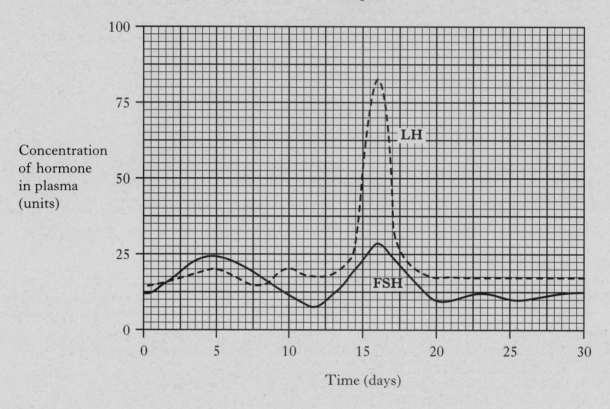

Graph 2

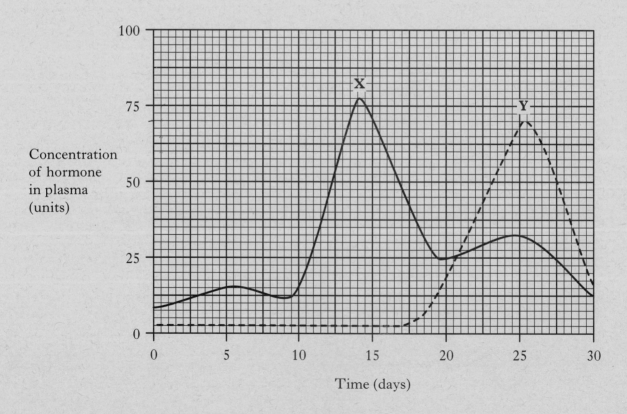

Marks

4. **(continued)**

(a) Where in the body are FSH and LH produced?

_____ 1

(b) Name hormones X and Y.

X _____

Y _____ 1

(c) What is the maximum concentration of hormone Y?

_____ units 1

(d) On which day did ovulation occur? Give a reason for your answer.

Day _____ 1

Reason _____

_____ 1

(e) During her next cycle, the woman became pregnant.

Describe any differences which would occur in the concentrations of FSH and hormone Y after day 25.

FSH _____

_____ 1

Hormone Y _____

_____ 1

[Turn over

Marks

5. (*a*) The table shows average quantities of substances filtered and excreted by the kidney per day.

Substance	Quantity filtered per day	Quantity excreted per day	Quantity reabsorbed per day
Water	$180\,dm^3$	$1\cdot5\,dm^3$	
Glucose	175 g	0 g	
Urea	48 g	31 g	
Protein	0 g	0 g	0 g

(i) Complete the table by calculating the quantities reabsorbed per day for water, glucose and urea.

1

(ii) What percentage of water filtered by the kidney is reabsorbed?

Space for calculation

_____ %   1

(iii) In which part of the kidney tubule is glucose reabsorbed?

_____   1

(*b*) Nephrosis is a kidney condition in which glomeruli are damaged.

As a result of nephrosis, the quantity of soluble proteins in the blood decreases and there is a build up of tissue fluid in the body.

(i) Explain why damage to the glomeruli results in a decrease of soluble protein in the blood.

_____

_____   1

(ii) Suggest a reason for the build-up of tissue fluid in the body.

_____

_____   1

Marks

6. The graph shows average blood pressure in different types of blood vessels.

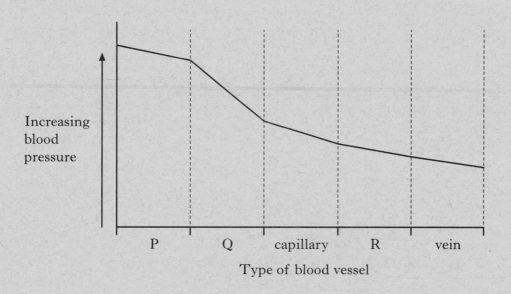

(a) Name the types of blood vessel represented by P, Q and R.

P _____

Q _____

R _____   2

(b) Blood pressure values fluctuate in vessel type P.

Explain the reason for this.

_____

_____   1

(c) Explain why there is a large drop in blood pressure in vessel type Q.

_____

_____

_____   1

(d) In the vena cava, blood pressure falls below atmospheric air pressure yet blood is still able to return to the heart.

Explain how the blood flow is maintained.

_____

_____

_____

_____   2

7. An investigation was carried out to find out how a cyclist's metabolism changed while he pedalled at increasing speed.

The cyclist's heart rate, fat and carbohydrate consumption were measured at different power outputs.

The graph below shows the results of the investigation.

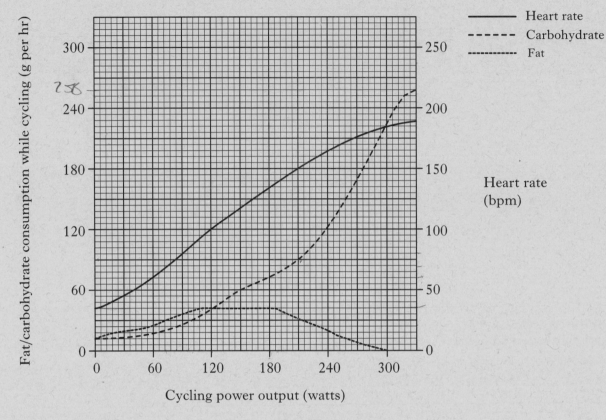

(a) What is the heart rate of the cyclist when his power output is 90 watts?

_____ bpm

1

(b) What evidence is there from the graph that the cyclist is very fit?

_____

_____

1

(c) Compare the consumption of fat and carbohydrate as cycling power increases. Quote data from the graph in your answer.

_____

_____

_____

_____

_____

_____

_____

3

Marks

7. (continued)

(*d*) (i) Cyclists often use heart-rate monitors in training. A cyclist wishes to maintain his fat consumption at its maximum and, at the same time, limit his carbohydrate consumption.

At what heart rate should he cycle?

_____ bpm

1

(ii) Suggest why it is good practice in a long distance cycling race to maximise fat consumption and minimise carbohydrate consumption.

_____

_____

_____

1

(*e*) The cyclist raced for 4 hours at a power output of 210 watts. During that time he consumed 100 g of carbohydrate in a liquid drink. Assuming he started with a carbohydrate store of 500 g, how much carbohydrate would he be left with at the end of the race?

Space for calculation

_____ g

1

(*f*) (i) Glycogen is a major source of carbohydrate. Where is glycogen stored in the body?

_____

1

(ii) Name a hormone which promotes the conversion of glycogen to glucose.

_____

1

(iii) What substance is used as a source of energy after glycogen and fat stores have been used up?

_____

1

[Turn over

DO NOT
WRITE IN
THIS
MARGIN

Marks

8. The diagrams below show two possible ways of classifying the nervous system.

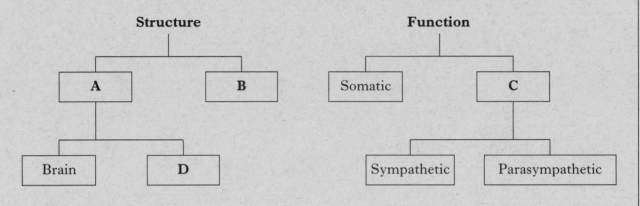

(a) (i) Identify A to D.

A _____

B _____

C _____

D _____ 2

(ii) Describe **one** function of the somatic nervous system.

_____

_____

_____ 1

(b) The brain contains two cerebral hemispheres.

(i) Name the structure which links these two hemispheres.

_____ 1

(ii) The surfaces of the hemispheres are heavily folded to provide a large surface area.

Explain the significance of this feature.

_____

_____

_____ 1

Marks

8. **(continued)**

(c) The diagram below shows some of the nerve connections between the brain and three parts of the body.

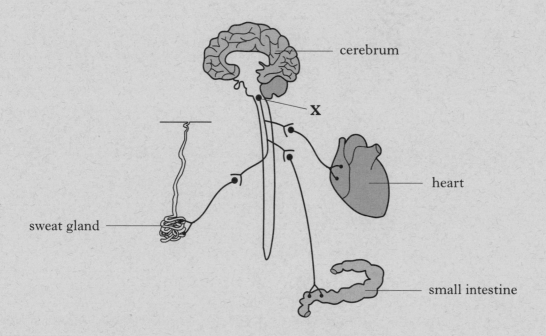

(i) Identify the part of the brain labelled **X**.

_____

1

(ii) The sympathetic and parasympathetic systems are often described as antagonistic to one another.

Explain the meaning of *antagonistic*.

_____

_____

1

(iii) Complete the table to show the effect of sympathetic stimulation on the heart, sweat glands and small intestine.

Part of body	*Sympathetic effect*
Heart	
Sweat glands	
Small intestine	

2

[Turn over

Marks

9. The diagram shows how a non-biodegradable insecticide passes through a food chain in a Scottish fresh-water loch.

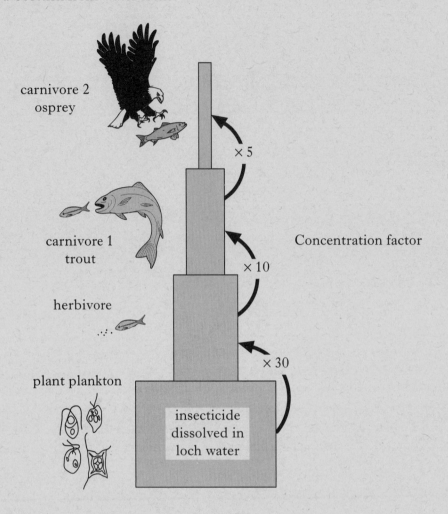

carnivore 2
osprey

× 5

carnivore 1
trout

Concentration factor

× 10

herbivore

× 30

plant plankton

insecticide
dissolved in
loch water

(a) Describe **one** way in which the insecticide could get into the loch water.

_____

_____

_____ 1

(b) (i) The diagram shows the number of times the insecticide becomes concentrated at each stage of the food chain.

If the concentration of insecticide in the plant plankton is 0·025 ppm what would be the expected concentration in the osprey?

Space for calculation

_____ ppm 1

Marks

9. **(b)** **(continued)**

(ii) Explain why insecticide becomes more concentrated in carnivores at the top of the food chain.

_____

_____

_____

_____

2

(c) DDT is an insecticide which breaks down slowly at a rate of 50% every fifteen years. Calculate how long it would take for 100 kg of DDT to break down to less than 1 kg.

Space for calculation

_____ years **1**

(d) Insecticides are chemicals used extensively in agriculture.

Name **two** other types of chemical used to treat crops and explain why they are used.

Chemical 1 _____

Use _____

_____ **1**

Chemical 2 _____

Use _____

_____ **1**

(e) Some insecticides work by disrupting enzyme-catalysed pathways.

What term is used to describe their action on enzymes?

_____ **1**

[Turn over

10. An experiment was carried out to investigate the effect of pH on the activity of the enzyme pepsin.

Marks

Six beakers were filled with pepsin solution and the pH adjusted in each beaker to give a range from pH 1 to pH 9. Six glass tubes were filled with egg albumen and boiled in water to set the egg white. The starting lengths of the egg white were measured and recorded in the table below.

The glass tubes were placed in the pepsin solution for a number of hours to allow digestion of the egg white. The lengths of egg white left in each tube at the end of the investigation are shown in the diagram below.

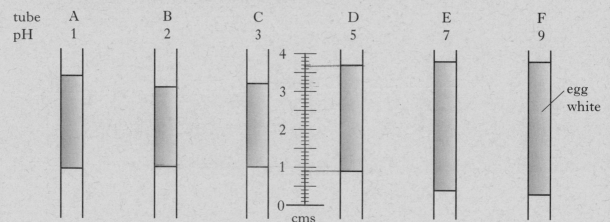

Tube	pH of pepsin solution	Length of egg white at start (mm)	Length of egg white at finish (mm)	Percentage decrease in length (%)
A	1	36	24	33
B	2	35	20	43
C	3	36		
D	5	34		
E	7	36	34	6
F	9	35	35	0

(a) (i) Complete the table above by measuring and recording the final lengths of egg white in tubes C and D.

1

(ii) Calculate the percentage decrease in length of egg white in tubes C and D and complete the table.

1

(b) Draw a line graph to show the relationship between pH and percentage decrease in length of egg white.

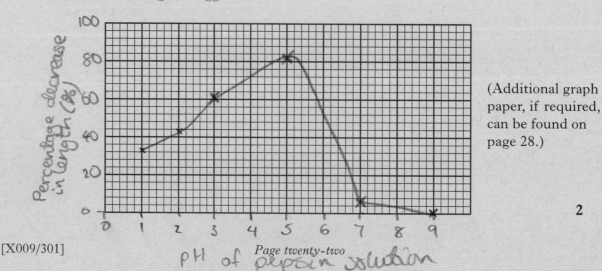

(Additional graph paper, if required, can be found on page 28.)

2

Marks

10. **(continued)**

(c)   (i)   What conclusion can be drawn from the results of this experiment?

_____

_____   1

(ii)   Predict the percentage decrease in length of egg white in a pepsin solution of pH 12.

_____   1

(iii)   Why was it necessary to calculate a *percentage* decrease?

_____

_____   1

(iv)   Describe a suitable control for tube **A** in this investigation.

_____

_____   1

(v)   State **three** variables which would have to be kept constant throughout this investigation.

1 _____

2 _____

3 _____   2

(vi)   Describe **one** way in which the results could be made more reliable.

_____

_____   1

(d)   Pepsin is produced in an inactive form by cells lining the stomach.

Why is it important that pepsin is inactive when it is produced?

_____

_____

_____   1

[Turn over

DO NOT
WRITE I
THIS
MARGII

SECTION C

Both questions in this section should be attempted.

Note that each question contains a choice.

Questions 1 and 2 should be attempted on the blank pages which follow.

Supplementary sheets, if required, may be obtained from the invigilator.

Labelled diagrams may be used where appropriate.

Marks

1. Answer **either** A **or** B.

   A. Give an account of temperature regulation in cold conditions under the following headings:

       (i)   voluntary responses;   **3**

       (ii) involuntary responses;   **5**

       (iii) hypothermia.   **2**

       (10)

   OR

   B. Give an account of the development of boys at puberty under the following headings:

       (i)   physical changes;   **3**

       (ii) hormonal changes.   **7**

       (10)

In question 2, ONE mark is available for coherence and ONE mark is available for relevance.

2. Answer **either** A **or** B.

   A. Discuss how the impact of disease on the human population can be reduced.   **(10)**

   OR

   B. Describe the factors which influence the development of behaviour.   **(10)**

[END OF QUESTION PAPER]

SPACE FOR ANSWERS

Page twenty-five **[Turn over**

DO NOT
WRITE IN
THIS
MARGIN

SPACE FOR ANSWERS

SPACE FOR ANSWERS

Page twenty-seven **[Turn over**

DO NOT
WRITE IN
THIS
MARGIN

SPACE FOR ANSWERS

ADDITIONAL GRAPH PAPER FOR QUESTION 10(*b*)

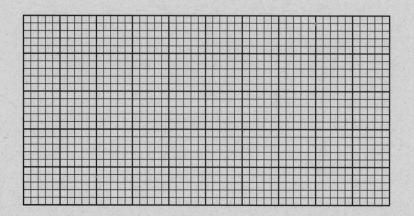

[BLANK PAGE]

[BLANK PAGE]

[BLANK PAGE]

[BLANK PAGE]